Whales

Their past, present and future

Philip Hammond, Sonja Heinrich,
Sascha Hooker and Peter Tyack

Published by the Natural History Museum, London

First published by the Natural History Museum,
Cromwell Road, London SW7 5BD
© The Trustees of the Natural History Museum, London, 2017

ISBN 978 0565 09412 6

A catalogue record for this book is available from the British Library

Designed by Mercer Design, London
Reproduction by Saxon Digital Services UK
Printed by Printer Trento Srl, Italy

FRONT COVER: © Maria Teresa Lara/500px; humpback calf, Tonga, South Pacific.

Contents

INTRODUCTION

What is a whale?

WHALES HOLD A SPECIAL FASCINATION for humans. They are sometimes considered as 'charismatic megafauna', meaning that they are very large, attractive animals that can inspire a special interest, or even devotion. Part of this appeal is that whales are very different from humans in some respects but very similar to us in others. They live in the alien and poorly known environments that are the world's seas and oceans, and most of us can only catch rare glimpses of them from our coasts or from a boat. But as mammals they share features with us, such as maintaining a warm body temperature and feeding their young with milk, and they display aspects of behaviour and intelligence comparable to those of humans, such as accumulating cultural knowledge that they pass from generation to generation.

Charisma can also result in people uniting in a common cause, and whales have become figureheads in environmental conservation efforts in the face of intense human pressures on our planet. As Sir Peter Scott told a meeting of the International Whaling Commission in 1972: 'if we can't save the largest animals in the world, we have little chance of saving the biosphere itself and therefore of saving our own species'. Whales have become flagship species in the battle to protect our planet against ourselves.

In some respects, whales can be seen as indicators of the health of ocean ecosystems because of their position at, or near, the top of marine food chains. Some people consider whales as sentinel species that can alert humans to problems in the marine environment or as bellwethers that are indicative of wider trends. This may be appropriate in some circumstances, but, as we shall see, whales have evolved over a long period and a wide range of conditions and are well equipped to deal with environmental variability. They are, however, not well equipped to deal with increased mortality resulting from human activities.

Whales are *marine* mammals that are adapted in a number of important ways to an aquatic life. Compared to land, the marine environment inhabited by whales is devoid of air and is thermally conductive, viscous, subject to high pressure and difficult to see in. Whales have developed enhanced diving capabilities to cope with obtaining their oxygen at the surface and their food underwater, sometimes at great

OPPOSITE A gray whale emerging from the water in a behaviour known as spyhopping. These whales migrate from their summer feeding grounds in the Arctic to lagoons off Baja California, Mexico to breed each winter.

depth. They can store a lot more oxygen in their blood and muscles than terrestrial mammals can, enabling them to maximise the time they spend underwater.

Whales are truly sub-surface creatures, spending the large majority of their lives under water away from where we can easily observe them. Yet we have been able to unravel some of their hidden behaviours with the ingenious use of modern tools and technologies. We can now eavesdrop on whales communicating with each other over hundreds of kilometres or listen to the sounds they make during a foraging dive. We can track the ocean-wide movements of large baleen whales during their annual migrations from the poles to the tropics, but also study the complex social communities of coastal dolphins.

WHAT'S IN A NAME?

The word 'whale' can be used as a general term to describe the group of animals known as cetaceans, which include all species of whales, dolphins and porpoises. However, it is more typically used as a common name for the largest species of cetacean, such as the blue whale, the largest animal ever to have lived on Earth, or the sperm whale. In this book, we use the word 'whale' in both senses – either interchangeably with 'cetacean' to mean whales, dolphins and porpoises in general, or to refer to those species that are commonly called whales.

The blue whale is a baleen whale, or mysticete, distinguished by having large structures called baleen plates instead of teeth. Baleen is used for filtering zooplankton, such as krill, or fish from huge mouthfuls of water. The baleen is made of keratin (the same material that hair and fingernails are made from). The sperm whale is the largest of the toothed whales, or odontocetes, which also includes dolphins

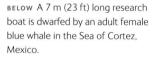
BELOW A 7 m (23 ft) long research boat is dwarfed by an adult female blue whale in the Sea of Cortez, Mexico.

and porpoises. The killer whale and the pilot whale, for example, are both members of the dolphin family. In total, there are 75 species in nine families of toothed whales and 14 species in four families of baleen whales alive today; this diversity is illustrated below. The evolution of these different types of whales and their modern family tree are described in Chapter 1.

All living organisms, including whales, are classified according to a system introduced by Swedish botanist Carl Linnaeus in the 1750s. The main levels of classification (known as taxonomic ranks) are kingdom, phylum, class, order, family, genus and species. All whales belong to the animal kingdom, the phylum of vertebrates (animals with backbones), the class of mammals (mentioned above and described in more detail in chapter 1) and the order of Cetartiodactyla (whales and hoofed land mammals). The genus and the species make up the formal binomial (two part) name of a particular species, such as *Balaenoptera musculus*, the blue whale. Binomial names are always written in italics with a capital for the first letter of the genus.

Kingdom – Animals

Phylum – Vertebrates

Class – Mammals

Order – Cetartiodactyla

Family – Balaenopteridae

Genus – *Balaenoptera*

Species – *musculus*

1 Blue whale
2 Sperm whale
3 Humpback whale
4 Gray whale
5 Killer whale
6 Narwhal
7 Beluga
8 Bottlenose dolphin
9 Harbour porpoise

LEFT Whales all have similar shapes but they come in a wide range of sizes from the 30 m (98½ ft) blue whale to the 1.5 m (5 ft) harbour porpoise.

RIGHT The term 'whale' can be used as the common name for all cetaceans, and so includes species such as this Amazon river dolphin in the Rio Negro, Brazil.

BELOW A group of long-finned pilot whales (members of the dolphin family) in typically close formation in the Alboran Sea, western Mediterranean.

STRUCTURE OF THIS BOOK

This book is about the biology of whales, including dolphins and porpoises, and how they have been, and continue to be, affected by human activities. In Chapter 1 we discuss some of the evolutionary changes to the terrestrial mammalian body and habits that have enabled whales to adapt to the challenge of an aquatic life and so successfully colonise the oceans. In Chapter 2 we describe the different climatic and ecological zones on Earth, how the diversity of whale species take advantage of the habitats available in these different bodies of water and illustrate how some species are very abundant but others are very rare. Chapter 3 introduces how whales live their lives, covering the topics of reproduction, growth, ageing and death, and describes the migratory behaviour displayed by most of the baleen whales. Chapter 4 focuses on the remarkable breath-holding and deep-diving capabilities of whales. Chapter 5 describes the different ways in which whales find and consume food, and how whales are an important part of marine ecosystems. In Chapter 6, we explore one aspect of the social behaviour of whales by introducing the topic of whale culture. Chapter 7 describes how human attitudes to whales have changed, from treating them as a commodity to be exploited to valuing them as species of ecological importance to be conserved. In Chapter 8, we discuss current and future pressures and threats to whales, including fisheries, chemical and noise pollution, and climate change.

WHY THIS BOOK ABOUT WHALES?

Whales look good in front of the camera and feature prominently in the media. Almost everyone will have seen a documentary about aspects of their remarkable lives. Many of us might even have been fortunate enough to glimpse a whale at sea, and a few of us will have experienced an up-close-and-personal encounter. There are also many books about whales. So why add to the existing wealth of printed material available on these animals?

We have written this book with two aims in mind: to offer you, the interested reader, an eight-course menu of up-to-date information about whales with more depth and diversity than is usually found in the popular literature; and to whet your appetite for taking an interest in protecting the ocean realm that whales and we depend on for survival.

Each chapter is a crash course in some essential aspects of whale biology or how whales interact with humans. We invite you to join us on a whirlwind time travel through 50 million years of evolution, on a round-the-world voyage to the marine environments of our planet, and on a breath-taking plunge to the greatest ocean depths. You will encounter the largest creatures to have roamed this planet and find out about how some of the smallest whales are struggling to avoid extinction. You will hear about whale song competitions and meet families whose social complexities rival our own. And you will be confronted with the challenges ahead to ensure that whales remain as integral components of marine ecosystems.

CHAPTER 1

There and back again

LIFE ON EARTH ORIGINATED in the primeval seas more than 3.5 billion years ago as simple single cells. It took a further 1.7 billion years until the first multicellular organisms appeared. Life forms in the sea began to diversify more than 500 million years ago, including the emergence of the very first vertebrates (animals with backbones) – a group that now comprises all fish and tetrapods (four-legged animals). Around 375 million years ago, fish with flexible fins that could support their body weight were the first creatures to crawl onto land. These lobe-finned fish became the ancestors of all tetrapods – the amphibians, reptiles, birds and mammals. Continental plates kept moving, the Earth's climate kept changing, new environments and selection pressures kept arising. For 160 million years, dinosaurs ruled the Earth, both on land and in the sea. After their extinction around 65 million years ago, mammals emerged as the most diverse and successful class of animals on land. But it was not until 50 million years ago, during the Eocene period, that a group of hoofed mammals took the first tentative steps back into the sea. Resources were rich and under-exploited in the warm shallow waters of the Tethys Sea (roughly corresponding to today's location of Pakistan and India), offering these terrestrial whale ancestors unique opportunities to expand their range into the aquatic realm.

ORIGIN OF WHALES

The first whales, archaeocetes, bore all the characteristics of land mammals. They had teeth typical of carnivores and walked on four legs with even-toed hoofs. One of the earliest archaeocetes, *Pakicetus,* did not look much like a whale, but its skull already had thick bony walls around the middle ear, which is a key feature of whales alive today and sets them apart from terrestrial mammals. *Pakicetus* means 'Pakistani whale' and is named after the location where the first fossils were found on which the description of this new lineage of archaeocete is based. The fossil evidence places the origin of *Pakicetus* in the Tethys Sea.

Some evolutionary steps and several million years later, *Ambulocetus* (also discovered in Pakistan) already showed signs of a more aquatic lifestyle. It had shorter legs with enlarged paddle-like feet and lived in estuaries at the interface

OPPOSITE These leaping Chilean dolphins (male in front, female at the back) show all the external characteristics of mammals fully adapted to life in the ocean.

ABOVE Fossil finds like this almost complete *Dorudon* skeleton (seen from below) are crucial for tracing the evolutionary steps that terrestrial mammals underwent to adapt to a fully aquatic life style.

of freshwater and marine environments. By the time *Dorudon* emerged, some 40 million years ago, archaeocetes were fully aquatic, living in saltwater and unable to return to land. *Dorudon* swam by undulating its whole body, had much reduced, dysfunctional hind limbs and shortened, stiffened front limbs that were used for steering. The nasal openings had started to move from the tip of the snout towards the top of the head. All in all, *Dorudon* looked a lot like modern whales. However, it is not a direct ancestor of them but belonged to a parallel lineage that went extinct. Such parallel lineages are depicted by the separate lines in the evolutionary history tree for whales shown opposite. Another example is the hippopotamus, an even-toed hoofed mammal, which is the closest living relative of whales on land, but its evolutionary path is very different from that of the cetaceans.

Fossil findings provide great insights into the anatomical features of past animals, but they do not necessarily represent the direct ancestors from which a modern form derived (see the box on fossils on page 14). The ancestors of modern baleen and toothed whales emerged during the 'icehouse world' in the Oligocene period some 35 million years ago; little is known about these animals because of gaps in the fossil record. This icehouse world was substantially colder and drier than the 'greenhouse world', when the first archaeocetes evolved. The colder climatic conditions and changes in oceanic circulation patterns influenced primary productivity on a global scale and created new and abundant prey fields. Early baleen whales, such as *Janjucetus* and *Mammalodon*, were small – less than 4 m (13 ft) long, still relied on teeth to catch prey, and had very little baleen. Filter feeding using baleen plates gradually helped the early baleen whales to exploit new and smaller prey types, such

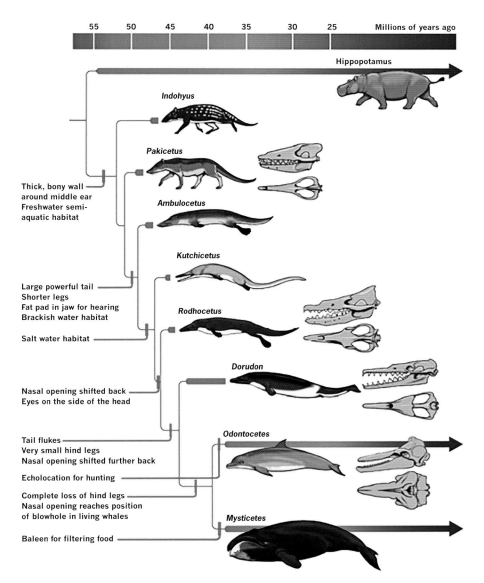

55   50   45   40   35   30   25   Millions of years ago

Hippopotamus

Indohyus

Pakicetus

Thick, bony wall
around middle ear
Freshwater semi-
aquatic habitat

Ambulocetus

Kutchicetus

Large powerful tail
Shorter legs
Fat pad in jaw for hearing
Brackish water habitat

Rodhocetus

Salt water habitat

Dorudon

Nasal opening shifted back
Eyes on the side of the head

Odontocetes

Tail flukes
Very small hind legs
Nasal opening shifted further back

Echolocation for hunting

Complete loss of hind legs
Nasal opening reaches position
of blowhole in living whales

Mysticetes

Baleen for filtering food

as zooplankton, and acquire large quantities of food efficiently in a short period. Such filter feeding on energy-dense prey enabled baleen whales to grow and attain the large body sizes of modern whales.

Echolocation (the ability to sense objects in the environment using sonar) is a key adaptation in toothed whales and distinguishes them from baleen whales. Echolocation opened up new food sources in deeper and darker waters because toothed whales no longer relied on light and sight to navigate and find food. As baleen whales evolved to bulk feed in the surface layers, early toothed whales started to explore the untapped resources of squid and fish, particularly in the deep ocean. The fossil record indicates that early deep diving beaked and sperm whales diversified rapidly around 15 million years ago, and today's species represent only a fraction of the past diversity.

ABOVE The evolutionary history of whales from terrestrial ancestors to fully aquatic modern whales. The separate branches for the archaeocetes (*Indohyus*, *Pakicetus*, *Ambulocetus*, *Kutchicetus*, *Rodhocetus* and *Dorudon*) indicate that the direct whale ancestors are not known yet.

FOSSILS – RECREATING EVOLUTIONARY HISTORY

While building an extension to the famous Pan-American Highway across the Atacama Desert in northern Chile in 2011, workers made a stunning discovery – fossil whale bones. They had stumbled onto the largest whale graveyard ever found. Over 15 busy days, palaeontologists unearthed 15 almost complete skeletons of ancient whales dating back seven million years. This find, along with subsequent ones, showed that the fossil whales had died en masse during four separate events over a period of several thousand years, representing a substantial part of the species diversity known for that period. These past mass die-offs are thought to be related to a phenomenon that still occurs off the coast of Chile today – blooms of toxic algae. Whales can ingest the toxins from the algae via their prey and die from the effects of poisoning. Sick whales from the same feeding grounds probably moved towards shallow waters, where they succumbed and became covered by marine sediments, only to be unearthed seven million years later to add important pieces to the whales' evolutionary jigsaw.

Extinction has erased much of the historical evidence of whale evolution. Fossils provide rare hard evidence of past animals' anatomical features, which can then be compared to those of modern species to identify differences and similarities. Fossils can also be dated and placed into the context of Earth's history, allowing past ecosystems and environments to be reconstructed. Two dating techniques are commonly used. Relative dating looks at the different rock and sediment layers surrounding the fossil and based on their age infers when the fossilized animal died. Absolute dating determines the amount of radioactive decay in rock or fossil minerals to estimate their time of deposit.

Fossils are crucial to fill the gaps in the whales' evolutionary tree, but can also be difficult to fit into the correct place. A particular challenge is to distinguish between ancestral lineages that led to modern whales and parallel lineages that went extinct. The mesonychids, an extinct group of wolf-like mammals with hoofs, had skulls and teeth that were very similar to archaeocetes and modern whales. They were thus believed to be a direct ancestor of whales. However, the discovery in 2001 of well-preserved hind limbs in archaeocetes (in particular a double pulley ankle bone) placed the archaeocetes into a separate lineage and linked them more closely to even-toed hoofed mammals (artiodactyls) than the mesonychids. Thus, the hippopotamus is the land-mammal most closely related to whales, and both are placed in the same order Cetartiodactyla (cetaceans and artiodactyls).

BELOW Scientists carefully unearth multiple fossil whale skeletons in northern Chile.

FAMILY TREE OF MODERN WHALES

Today's whale species represent only a subset of the past diversity of toothed and baleen whales. The 89 currently recognized species are spread over 13 families, with toothed whales, collectively called odontocetes, still showing great diversity in the number of families (nine) and species (75), with a wide range of body sizes and behaviours. The 14 baleen whale species, collectively called mysticetes, are spread over four families, with eight of those species belonging to the rorqual family (balaenopterids). There is only one species of gray whale and one of pygmy right whale (which are the only existing members of their respective families). The remaining four baleen whale species belong to the right whale family (balaenids), which is the least abundant group of all whales. This is a legacy of the very intense whaling of right whales, which were so named because they were literally the 'right' whales to hunt (see page 111).

However, the only whale species to go extinct since humans have been walking on the planet is the baiji, or Yangtze river dolphin, which was only a little bigger than the tallest human. As the name suggests, the baiji inhabited the Yangtze river in China, where it evolved at least 10 million years ago. The last confirmed sighting of a baiji was in 2004. Scientific surveys in 2006 found none and the species was officially declared 'functionally extinct', which means that it can no longer fulfil a role in the natural environment and be sustained as a species in the wild (the last one in captivity had died in 1996). The loss of the baiji constitutes an important loss of evolutionary history because it was the only surviving species in the family *Lipotidae*, which was one of the most ancient lineages of toothed whales.

BELOW The baiji, or Yangtze river dolphin, lived only in China and is now probably extinct. This image of a now deceased captive dolphin shows its characteristic features of small eyes and a long narrow snout.

BELOW Relatedness tree of the modern cetacean families: the shorter the line distances between families the more closely related these are.

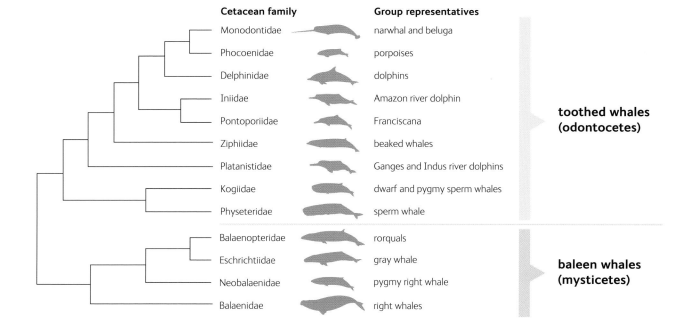

Cetacean family	Group representatives
Monodontidae	narwhal and beluga
Phocoenidae	porpoises
Delphinidae	dolphins
Iniidae	Amazon river dolphin
Pontoporiidae	Franciscana
Ziphiidae	beaked whales
Platanistidae	Ganges and Indus river dolphins
Kogiidae	dwarf and pygmy sperm whales
Physeteridae	sperm whale
Balaenopteridae	rorquals
Eschrichtiidae	gray whale
Neobalaenidae	pygmy right whale
Balaenidae	right whales

toothed whales (odontocetes)

baleen whales (mysticetes)

THE MOLECULAR CLOCK AND GENETIC FINGERPRINTS OF EVOLUTIONARY TREES

The evolutionary history of each species is recorded in its DNA (genetic material). The molecular clock is a technique used to measure the timing of evolutionary changes based on the number of changes, or mutations, that accumulate in the DNA of a species over time. Genetic mutations are random and over long periods are assumed to occur at a relatively constant rate so that the number of differences between two gene sequences increases over evolutionary time. A normal clock measures time from regular changes (the ticks on the dial), but a molecular clock measures time based upon random changes (mutations) in the DNA. Any clock has to be calibrated before it can work. Setting the molecular clock requires a known reference point in time, such as from fossil or geological records. Then, once mutation rate is determined, the time of divergence of a species can be calculated; for example, if the mutation rate is five mutations every million years, and we count 25 mutations in the DNA sequence, then we know that the sequence diverged 5 million years ago.

The molecular clock can be used to establish the order of evolutionary events by comparing DNA sequences from different species to determine when they last shared a common ancestor. This is how molecular evolutionary trees are derived. An example of such a molecular tree is shown here for killer whales on a global scale. Genetic samples taken from modern living killer whales form the outer ring of the tree. Each individual whale is represented by a dash (i.e. the leaves of the tree) and is connected by lines (i.e. branches) to other whales. The more branches that separate two whales the more distant those whales' lineages are. Thus, genetic relatedness is mapped as distance along the tree's branches. The most basal killer whale lineages are located towards the centre and represent the tree trunk. The colour codes represent the ocean basins where the individual whales were sampled. This geographic information can be combined with the molecular clock to estimate the time of divergence (i.e. when one lineage separated into two) and infer the direction of dispersal from one ocean basin to another. Thus, the molecular tree provides a visual representation of the complex ancestral pattern and diversity of modern killer whales.

There are still many problems with molecular clocks, and the estimated timelines are usually approximate, with errors that can often be quite large. If the information for the calibration points used to set the clock is wrong or imprecise, then this can lead to the clock being out by millions of years. The clock also does not tick in years but in generation times, which differ between species and are not easily inferred for ancestral species.

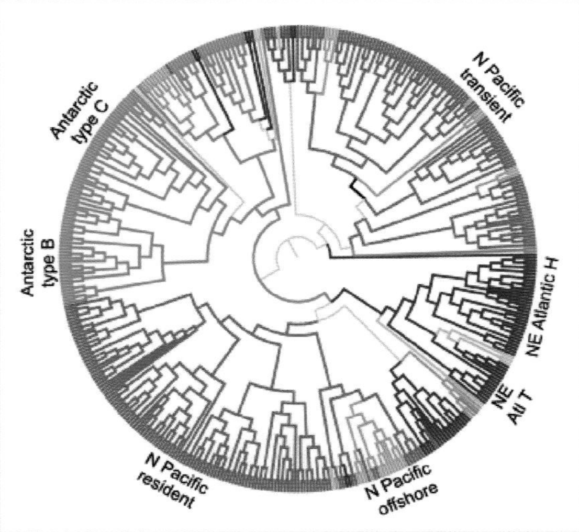

LEFT The evolutionary tree for killer whales from different regions of the world showing when and how current populations are thought to have diverged, which allows colonization patterns to be inferred. Colour represents the geographic location where the individual whales were sampled:

red = North Pacific
orange = Tropical Pacific
purple = South Pacific
dark blue = North Atlantic
light blue = South Atlantic
pink = Indian Ocean
green = Southern Ocean

BEING A WHALE

When the ancestors of whales returned to a fully aquatic lifestyle, this required reshaping the body and many of its internal functions, while being constrained by the core characteristics that define mammals. Whales, like other mammals, have a stable core body temperature which they are able to maintain in spite of changes in the ambient temperature. They give birth to live young after a lengthy period of development inside the female's uterus. Young whales are suckled with milk secreted from the female's mammary glands, in a process called lactation, which can last from months to years depending on the whale species (see page 59). All mammals breathe air into paired lungs, where oxygen is extracted from the air and passed into the blood to be transported around the body. Oxygen is a key element in metabolic processes of the body, because it is needed in biochemical reactions to produce energy efficiently in all cells.

Compared with terrestrial environments, the oceans conduct heat 25 times better than air and are viscous, have low levels of oxygen, are murky at the surface and dark at depth, where the pressure is tens of times greater than at the surface. Thus, at first glance, the oceans are not an ideal environment for mammals. However, whales have managed to adapt to these challenges in remarkable ways, including holding their breath for extended periods of up to two hours when diving and coping with the crushing pressure at depth (see page 70).

Whales are huge compared to terrestrial mammals. Even the smallest dolphin is the size and weight of a small adult human. The biggest whales, such as blue, fin and sperm whales, are at least 15–20 times the size of the largest land mammal, the African elephant. Being big helps whales and dolphins cope with loss of heat, prolonged periods of breath-holding and fasting. Bigger animals have a smaller surface to volume ratio (and so lose less heat), have lower energy requirements relative to body mass, and can store more vital resources such as fat or oxygen.

These benefits of being bigger in the ocean do not fully explain why some whales became so enormous. It is the buoyancy of water that removes, for marine mammals, one of the fundamental constraints on size of all land animals. Whales float and do not have to carry their huge weight or move it around on their legs. In fact, whales have lost their external hind limbs and only have vestigial pelvic bones. A recent study found that pelvic bones are not functionless relics, as previously thought, but instead support the whale genitalia and might play an important role during mating. For locomotion, whales have a robust tail that ends in a horizontal fluke that propels them forwards. The fluke itself does not contain bones but is made up of fibrous connective tissue that is highly vascularized (see page 28). Powerful muscles and tendons connect the fluke with the tail bones to allow the whale to generate forward thrust with forceful up–down strokes. The up–down motion of the fluke is different to the side-to-side movement of swimming fish, and is a legacy of the whale's land mammal origin. The backbones of four-legged mammals undulate in an up–down wave relative to the position of the head and the tail. Whales can be thought of as 'galloping' through the water in a similar way to giraffes galloping over the African savannah.

BELOW Main changes to the mammalian body plan in whales with the characteristics shown for a typical toothed whale (bottlenose dolphin – top) and a typical baleen whale (blue whale – bottom) with labels describing key features that distinguish toothed and baleen whales . The skeleton in the centre is labelled with generic whale features that are different from the terrestrial mammal body plan.

Unlike giraffes, though, whales have a very short, stiff neck that stabilizes their head and allows little or no head motion. Whales are surprisingly manoeuvrable thanks to front limbs that have transformed into paddle- or blade-shaped flippers with shorter bones and fixed elbow joints. Fast-swimming species such as blue, fin and sei whales have a highly elongated, streamlined body and small flippers, whereas slow but manoeuvrable swimmers such as humpback and right whales have a broader body with relatively large flippers.

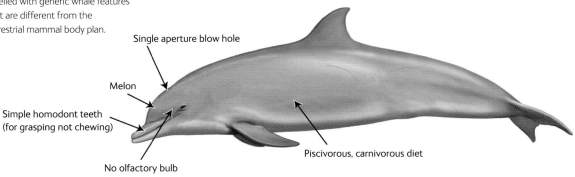

Single aperture blow hole

Melon

Simple homodont teeth
(for grasping not chewing)

No olfactory bulb

Piscivorous, carnivorous diet

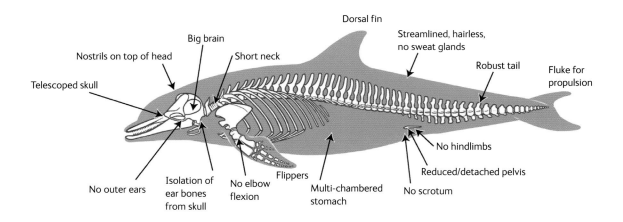

Dorsal fin

Big brain

Nostrils on top of head

Short neck

Streamlined, hairless,
no sweat glands

Telescoped skull

Robust tail

Fluke for
propulsion

No hindlimbs

No outer ears

Isolation of
ear bones
from skull

No elbow
flexion

Flippers

Multi-chambered
stomach

Reduced/detached pelvis

No scrotum

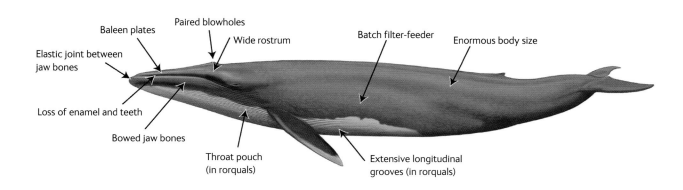

Baleen plates

Paired blowholes

Wide rostrum

Batch filter-feeder

Enormous body size

Elastic joint between
jaw bones

Loss of enamel and teeth

Bowed jaw bones

Throat pouch
(in rorquals)

Extensive longitudinal
grooves (in rorquals)

Humpback whale flippers can reach almost 5 m (16 ft) long (nearly one-third of their body length), and their genus name *Megaptera* aptly means 'great wings'. Right whales have much shorter but broader paddle-shaped flippers. Both species might use their flippers for temperature regulation (see page 28), in social interactions with conspecifics or in defence against predators, such as killer whales. Deep-diving species such as sperm or beaked whales have shallow indentations on their sides, almost like little pockets, allowing them to tuck their flippers against their body, possibly to reduce drag and energy expenditure when diving.

LEFT This Southern right whale breaching off Peninsula Valdes, Argentina re-enters the water on its back showing its almost rectangular-shaped flippers that increase manoeuvrability under water.

BELOW A humpback whale off the Antarctic Peninsula rolls onto its side and waves its long pectoral flipper which is nearly one-third the length of the entire animal.

All important aspects of the life of a whale take place underwater: finding food and feeding (see Chapters 4 and 5), mating, giving birth and suckling their young (see Chapter 3), and interacting socially (see Chapter 6). Yet whales must come to the surface to breathe air, and they have to hold their breath (called apnoea) when submerged. Whales consciously control when they take a breath, unlike most mammals, including humans, which are reflex breathers. When a whale's head reaches the surface after a dive, muscles pull open the blowhole or nares (the functional equivalent of the nostrils of other mammals). The air pressure in the nasal passage is higher than ambient pressure at the surface, leading to the explosive release of air from the blowhole. The exhaled air from the whale's inside is warmer than the surrounding air and carries moisture, which condenses into the visible blow that so often is the first tell-tale sign of a whale. Toothed whales have only one blowhole, whereas baleen whales have two. Baleen whales have a raised blowhole with a splash guard on the forward-facing side to prevent water from entering when the whale is inhaling while swimming. The shape and size of the blows differ among species and are used as diagnostic features when identifying whales at sea.

Whales, particularly the smaller dolphins and porpoises, keep swimming while taking a breath and may leap clear out of the water at speed. The cycle of explosive exhalation and equally rapid inhalation is completed in less than one second in smaller species (a few seconds in large whales), and is often audible to the human

BELOW A fin whale surfaces and exhales revealing its blowhole with splash guard and its tall columnar blow of up to 6 m (19½ ft) in height.

observer nearby. Such efficient breath-taking is aided by the position of the blowhole at the top of the head. The nostrils of most mammals are located towards the front of the skull at the tip of the snout. Over the whale's evolutionary history, the nostrils moved back and upwards to the top of the skull, substantially modifying the rostrum (snout) and adjacent bones – a process known as cranial telescoping. In a whale skull, the upper jawbones (maxillae and premaxillae) are elongated, the nasal bones have been pushed back, and the frontal skull section is much reduced.

The lower jaw in whales is also substantially different from that of other mammals. Baleen whales have separate right and left jawbones that are very long and curved. In lunge-feeding rorquals (balaenopterids), such as humpback and blue whales, the lower jawbones are connected to the skull by dense fibres and cartilage, allowing the lower jaw to swing open at a nearly 90 degree angle during a feeding lunge. The mouth cavity and pleated throat tissue on the underside extend, allowing a blue whale with one lunge to engulf and then filter a volume of prey-laden water that is equal to its own body volume and could fill a medium-sized swimming pool (around 60 m³, or 2,120 ft³) (see page 78). A recently discovered gelatinous sensory organ sits at the tip of the snout between the two lower jawbones and is thought to help coordinate the opening and closing of this massive mouth, which can be completed in fewer than 10 seconds.

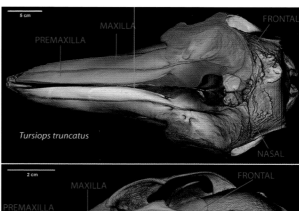

Tursiops truncatus

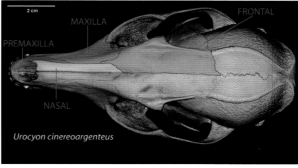

Urocyon cinereoargenteus

ABOVE Skulls of a bottlenose dolphin (top) and a grey fox (bottom) showing the difference in the position of the nasal openings and the condition of 'cranial telescoping' in whales. Bone structures that underwent major modifications are colour coded: orange – premaxilla; blue – maxilla; yellow – nasal; green – frontal.

LEFT A humpback whale lunges to the surface off Svalbard, Norway, with its mouth full of water and food, and its throat pleats extended.

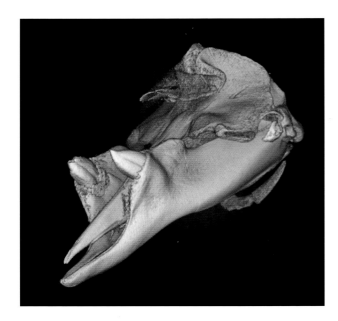

The lower jaws of toothed whales are fused at the tip. In some species, the lower jaws can be long and narrow in symmetry with the elongated upper jaws, forming a visible snout (as in the bottlenose dolphin) or even a long 'beak' (as in the beaked whales). Dolphins have uniformly conical teeth in both upper and lower jaws, whereas beaked whales have no functional teeth and feed using suction (see page 81). Among the beaked whales, only males develop two tusks, which erupt from the lower jaw and sometimes protrude well past the upper jaw as they do in Blainville's beaked whales. Beaked whales have very dense jawbones compared with other toothed whales, and Blainville's beaked whales are also called 'dense-beaked whales' (the species name is *densirostris*, or 'dense beak') because their jawbone is denser than elephant ivory. French zoologist Henri de Blainville, who gave the whale its common and Latin names, first described the species from a piece of jaw that was the heaviest bone he had ever come across. The combination of tusks in males, very dense jawbones and intense scarring on the body of these whales suggests that male beaked whales might engage in physical combat with other males to gain access to or defend reproductive females.

A distinguishing feature of toothed whales is asymmetry of their skull, with structures on one side consistently larger than those on the other side, which is a rare condition in mammals. In sperm whales this asymmetry is visible in a unique lop-sided blow, because the blowhole is located at an angle on the left side of the head. The function of this cranial asymmetry in sperm whales is related to sound production, but there may be other functions in other species.

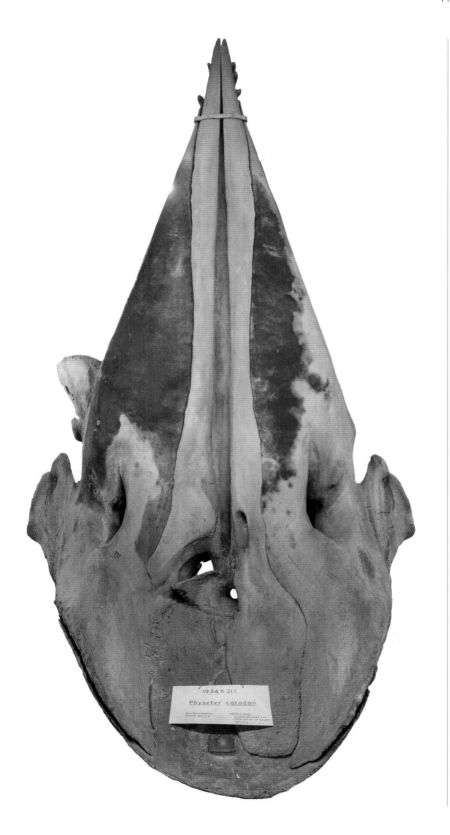

1934.6.21.1

Physeter catodon.

LEFT Dorsal view of a sperm whale skull (looking down from above), showing the basin-like region at the back of the skull (in which the specimen documentation is placed) and the long rostrum. Cranial asymmetry is visible in the differently sized openings of the bony narial tubes (the large left and smaller right holes in the middle of the skull). The left opening allows the passage of air between the blowhole, found only on the left in sperm whales, and the lungs.

COMING TO WHALE SENSES

In land mammals, the most important senses involve sight (eyes), smell (nose) and sound (ears). This is different for whales, because water is a very different medium from air. Sunlight does not penetrate the oceans much beyond a depth of 200 m (660 ft) because of the way water scatters light. Surface waters are often murky because of suspended particles, further reducing visibility to no more than tens of metres. Most whales have small but functional eyes adapted for vision in water, including slightly flattened eyeballs, enlarged pupils (which shrink as whales surface to prevent damage), slightly flattened corneas and a light-sensitive layer called the *tapetum lucidum*, which is also well established in night-active land mammals. These adaptations allow for large amounts of light to pass through the eye and provide a clear image in water. Whales can also see well in air over shorter ranges, but they are a little short-sighted out of the water.

Odour molecules diffuse more slowly in water than in air, making smell less efficient. Toothed whales have even lost the normal mammalian capacity to smell, because they no longer have an olfactory bulb (the nerve structure in the brain where smell is processed in mammals). Baleen whales still retain an auxiliary olfactory sense organ (the Jacobson's organ), which may be used to detect chemicals associated with some of their prey, such as krill.

Despite its shortcomings as a medium for light and chemical stimuli, water is a great medium for sound. The speed of sound is roughly four times greater in water than in air at sea level, and low-frequency sound waves can travel hundreds of kilometres through the oceans. It is thus not surprising that sound plays a key role in the lives of all whales.

Whales perceive their environment, communicate with each other and locate food using sound. Perceiving ambient sounds can be a passive process (listening), but using sounds for communication and echolocation necessitates active, purposeful sound emission. Baleen and toothed whales differ markedly in the types

RIGHT A whale's eye is small but well adapted for vision underwater. Sperm whale skin sloughs regularly as part of natural exfoliation to prevent encrusting by parasites or other marine animals.

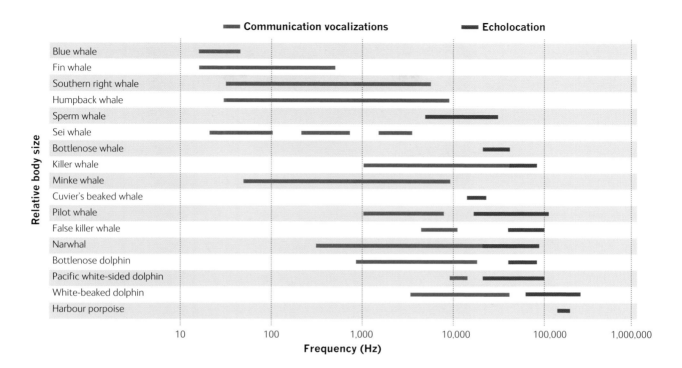

Communication vocalizations   Echolocation

Relative body size

Blue whale
Fin whale
Southern right whale
Humpback whale
Sperm whale
Sei whale
Bottlenose whale
Killer whale
Minke whale
Cuvier's beaked whale
Pilot whale
False killer whale
Narwhal
Bottlenose dolphin
Pacific white-sided dolphin
White-beaked dolphin
Harbour porpoise

10   100   1,000   10,000   100,000   1,000,000

Frequency (Hz)

of sounds they produce and how they produce them. Baleen whales vocalize in the very low frequency ranges (10s to 1000s of Hertz, and up to almost 10,000 Hertz in humpback and minke whales) with some of their sounds below the frequency range that humans can hear (i.e. 20 Hertz to up 20,000 Hertz in some young people). These low frequency vocalizations can be broadcast and heard by other whales over tens to hundreds of kilometres in the right conditions (see pages 104–106 and 130). How baleen whales make their low-frequency vocalizations is not well understood. The larynx (voice box) appears to play a role, as in other mammals (including humans in which it is so crucial for vocalization).

In contrast, toothed whales produce distinct types of vocalizations in much higher (often ultrasonic) frequency ranges: tonal and burst-pulsed sounds (500 Hertz to around 60,000 Hertz) and echolocation clicks (1,000 to 130,000 Hertz). These higher frequency sounds can only be used over hundreds of metres to several kilometres, so toothed whales have much smaller communication ranges than baleen whales. Toothed whale tonal sounds (such as dolphin whistles) and echolocation clicks are made by pushing air back and forth over vibrating pairs of structures called phonic lips, located in the airway directly below the blowhole. Much of the sound energy of a click is reflected off the skull forward into the melon, a large fatty organ situated directly in front of the phonic lips. The melon directs the sounds into a beam of sound useful for echolocation (much like the lens in a torch can be used to change the shape of the light beam). The melon contributes to the 'forehead' bulge of many toothed whales, especially the deep diving beaked, pilot and sperm whales.

ABOVE Vocalization ranges for a diversity of whale species. Larger whales produce lower frequency sounds for communication. Most toothed whales produce both communication sounds and higher frequency echolocation clicks.

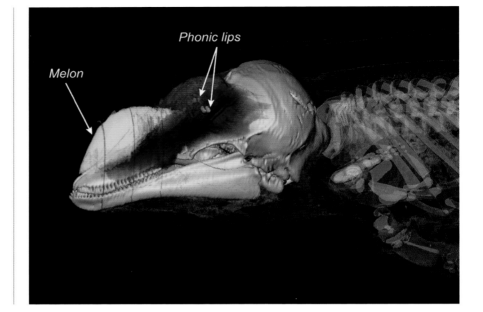

RIGHT Magnetic Resonance Imaging (MRI) scan of a porpoise showing the head with the melon (yellow) and connective tissue, muscles, and tendons (red). The phonic lips where clicks are produced are also shown.

BELOW Cross-section of the sperm whale head showing the spermaceti organ and junk located above and in front of the skull bones.

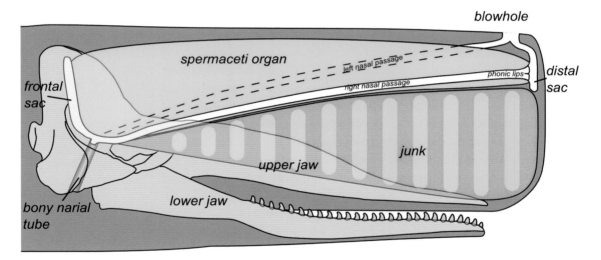

Sperm whale males have the largest head, proportional to body size, of all mammals. In some males the head can make up one-third of the entire body length. Early whalers mistook the spermaceti organ (a large organ filled with a liquid mixture of fats and waxes) in the sperm whale's head as the place where these whales stored their sperm – hence the name 'sperm whale'. The spermaceti organ was highly prized by the whalers because it could be rendered into high-quality oil (see page 112). The oil from a second fatty organ situated below the spermaceti organ was less valuable, and was therefore called 'junk'. We know now that the spermaceti organ and the junk (which functions to form a forward-directed beam of sound analogous to the melon found in other toothed whales) are crucial components in sound production in male and female sperm whales.

Sperm whales use echolocation clicks to locate their favourite food, squid and fish, at great ocean depths (see page 83). They also use a particular type of click (called coda) for social communication (see pages 84 and 108). The spermaceti organ and the size of the male's head are important for sperm whale reproduction – but not in the way that the whalers thought! Scientists now think that females can assess a male's body size by listening to the male's clicks. Bigger males produce louder clicks, and the click intervals give away the size of the whale's head. Bigger males might also be able to echolocate and identify prey further away, allowing them to increase foraging efficiency. Bigger seems to be better, at least for male sperm whales.

Sperm whales not only have the biggest head of all mammals in relation to overall body size, they also have the largest brain. However, brain size alone does not say much about an animal's intelligence or cognitive abilities. These also depend on the internal structuring of the brain and the relationship between brain size and body size. Humans have a more complex brain (with larger cortex volume) than any other animal. Brain complexity and relative size reflect the tasks an animal has to fulfil during its life. The social intelligence hypothesis suggests that social animals with complex social interactions and behaviours have the largest brains. Humans are clearly top of the list here, but toothed whales such as sperm whales, which live in social groups and rely on processing complex acoustic information (such as from communication and echolocation signals), are not too far behind.

Given that sounds are of such fundamental importance to whales, hearing is their most important sense. Whales do not have external ears and receive sounds through a different pathway from that of terrestrial mammals. In terrestrial mammals, sound passes through an air-filled canal from the outer to the middle ear, where vibrations in air are converted by the middle ear to vibrations that can more efficiently enter the fluid-filled inner ear. Whales already live in a fluid medium, so they can receive sounds from the water through their skin, passing sound through specialized fatty tissues directly to the inner ear. The inner ear of whales is not attached to the skull and is acoustically isolated by air-filled sinus pockets, which enable whales to have greater directional hearing underwater. High-frequency echoes returning from echolocation clicks enter the ear through the lower jaw, again passing through specialized fatty tissues directly to the inner ear. So, compared with terrestrial mammals, which use eyes to see and ears to hear, whales 'see' with sounds (i.e. echolocation) that can be heard through their lower jaw (see also page 82).

GETTING UNDER A WHALE'S SKIN

Most terrestrial and semi-aquatic mammals, such as seals or otters, rely on fur for insulation. Whales show signs of hair during foetal development, and some whale species sport some hairs or hair follicles on their head. But, by and large, whale skin is hairless and also lacks sweat glands. The skin tends to be thick, and the outer layers can slough off many times per day. Researchers collect such sloughed whale skin as a non-invasive means to get material for genetic analysis to study various aspects of whale biology. Whale skin also harbours its own unique bacterial microcosm, and the composition of this microbiome might be an indicator of the whale's health status. For example, whales exposed to antibiotics in the water or those that have become entangled in fishing gear (presumably a very stressful experience) have different microbiomes on their skin compared with whales in unaffected environments.

The tissue underneath a whale's skin (called blubber) was the main reason why many whale species were being hunted to the brink of extinction. Whale blubber was used to render oil for many purposes, especially for lighting, industrial use and cosmetics (see Chapter 7). The Inuit living in the high Arctic consider whale skin and blubber (*muktuk*) a vital source of nutrition and a staple in their diet. For the whales, blubber plays key roles in insulation and as an energy store. Blubber is so much more than just fat. Blubber is vascularized adipose tissue, which means that it contains fat (lipid) cells and elastic (collagen) fibres spanned by a network of small blood vessels. The thickness of the blubber layer of an individual whale changes seasonally, over its annual life cycle, and varies among species. The blubber layer ranges from 2 to 5 cm (¾ to 2 in) thick in dolphins and porpoises to more than 30 cm (12 in) thick in large whales, such as right and bowhead whales. The thickness of a whale's blubber layer is not so much influenced by the water temperature of the ocean as by a whale's life history. Baleen whales have to store energy accumulated at their polar feeding grounds for the lean periods in the tropics, where they reproduce but do not feed (see page 60). Blubber is a whale's 'savings account' for storing energy for times when food is scarce and energy is needed for special investment (such as suckling offspring). By contrast, the thinner blubber layer in toothed whales is mostly used for insulation; they do not fast for long periods and feed regularly while lactating (see page 63).

BELOW Aboriginal whalers process a bowhead whale for traditional food, especially *muktuk* consisting of blubber (pink) and skin (black). The blubber in bowhead whales can be up to 30 cm (1 ft) thick.

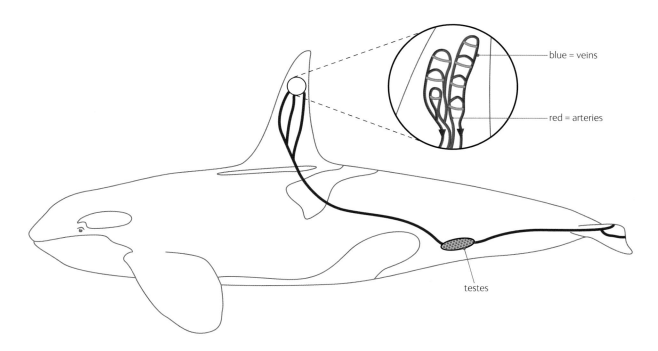

blue = veins

red = arteries

testes

For healthy whales, staying warm in cold water is not a problem because they are well insulated and generate enough metabolic heat from swimming to keep warm. Rather, whales often have the opposite problem – they can get too hot. The blubber layer is a good insulator and covers the whale's entire body except for the fins and fluke. So a whale's appendages play an important role in the regulation of their body temperature, which is achieved with an energy-efficient counter-current heat exchange system. In this system, heat is transferred between warm blood from the core flowing past colder blood returning from the surface layers. When a whale needs to keep warm, blood flow and heat exchange are regulated so that heat loss from the skin to the surrounding water is reduced. However, if a whale gets too hot it can increase the flow of warm blood from the core to the surface of its fluke and flippers (and also through the blubber) to dissipate heat.

Staying cool is particularly important for male whales. For streamlining and protection, a whale's reproductive organs are tucked inside the body, where the core temperature is around the typical mammalian 37°C (98.6°F). This is too warm to produce quality sperm, which is the main reason why most male mammals have their testes in a scrotum outside the body cavity. So, to keep the testes cool and maintain the right temperature for quality sperm production, a whale can cool blood at its fins or flukes, which then gets transported to the testes to keep them cool.

The move to a fully aquatic lifestyle has afforded opportunities for whales, but also challenges. Their biology and behaviour have been shaped by the environment in which different whale species live. The next chapters look more closely at the whales' habitats and habits.

ABOVE A whale can regulate its body temperature, including that of individual organs, by using heat exchange systems in the fluke and fins. The testes in male whales are located inside the body cavity and need to be kept cool to produce fertile sperm.

CHAPTER 2

Whales everywhere

From space, the planet is blue.
From space, the planet is the territory
Not of humans, but of the whale.

(lines taken from *Whale Nation* by Heathcote Williams)

WE HUMANS CONSIDER OURSELVES the most successful species of all time, having become established on all parts of planet Earth, and even reaching into outer space. We have explored all the world's oceans, and more recently have started to use our technological prowess to peek into some of the deepest ocean trenches. Yet the most versatile and successful explorers of the oceans, which cover almost 72% of the surface of our planet, are the whales. Cetaceans (whales, dolphins and porpoises) call all oceans their home, from the poles to the equator, from the shallow coastal waters to the great depths of the open ocean. This chapter looks at the different marine environments and how small and large whales use them. We also explore how we study where the whales are and how many whales there are in the oceans.

WHERE THE WHALES ARE – CLIMATIC ZONES

The distribution of whales can be described based on climatic zones as polar, temperate or tropical. Belugas, narwhals and bowhead whales are examples of polar species, which reside year-round in the cold seasonally ice-covered waters of the Arctic. Most baleen whale species visit the polar regions seasonally to feed and then migrate to temperate-tropical waters to breed (see page 60). Blue, fin, minke and humpback whales are typical examples of such cosmopolitan species living their lives across all climatic zones.

The tropical zone refers to the warm waters on either side of the equator, approximately between the Tropic of Cancer (23.5°N) and the Tropic of Capricorn (23.5°S). It is home to a diverse range of dolphin species, such as spinner or common dolphins, but of the larger whales only Bryde's whales and female sperm whales live

OPPOSITE Several species of dolphin use both nearshore and open-water habitats. Here, a group of spinner dolphins swims off the Kona coast of the Big Island of Hawaii in the central North Pacific.

RIGHT Whales inhabit different climatic zones and have different distribution patterns: a Bryde's whale swims with a group of common dolphins off South Africa (top), a blue whale surfaces off the coast of southern Chile (middle), and a bowhead whale breaches in the ice-covered Arctic Ocean, off Canada (bottom).

there year-round. The temperate zone is sandwiched between the tropical and polar regions, and often contains areas where cold polar and warm tropical waters mix, supporting a range of marine habitats. Many dolphin and most of the porpoise species inhabit temperate waters, particularly near the coasts. Large whales are common there too. Sei and right whales spend a lot of their time feeding in cool-temperate and sub-polar waters, and humpback, fin and blue whales pass through the temperate zone during their annual migrations, and also feed there.

Even in cosmopolitan species not all individuals roam across all climatic zones. Sperm whales inhabit the waters from the tropics to the polar regions. However, male and female sperm whales reside in different habitats for most of their lives. Females and calves live year-round at lower latitudes in tropical/temperate waters, where the risk of predation on calves is relatively low but food is also limited. Mature males spend most of their time feeding at higher latitudes in cold temperate and polar waters, but they migrate to lower latitudes to seek out females for mating (see page 63). This pattern of sexual segregation starts when young male sperm whales leave their family groups and move to the more productive temperate and

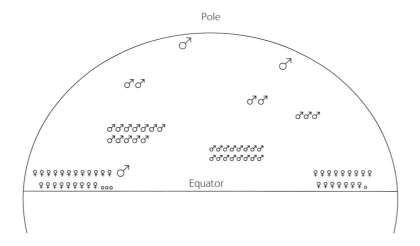

LEFT Male sperm whales spend most of their lives at higher latitudes towards the poles while females and young remain in lower latitudes near the Equator.

BELOW Male calves of sperm whale stay with their mothers for several years before moving towards the poles to feed and grow big. Female calves never leave tropical-temperate waters.

ABOVE A male sperm whale prepares for one of many feeding dives into the deep productive canyons off the Kaikoura coast, New Zealand.

polar waters to feed and grow. Size matters in male sperm whales because bigger males gain more mating opportunities. Bachelor males remain in temperate-polar waters until they are mature and big enough to compete for females. Such habitat segregation between the sexes is driven by different life history needs. By reducing competition for prey between females and males this may help individuals from either sex to maximize their reproductive success.

In contrast to globally roaming marine species, some dolphins and porpoises are confined to specific river systems – they are unique in that they live in freshwater year round and have very restricted distributional ranges. Species of river dolphins inhabit the Amazon (the boto, also known as the pink dolphin, and the tucuxi), the Ganges (the susu, or Ganges river dolphin) and the Indus (bhulan, or Indus river dolphin). As we saw in Chapter 1, the baiji has disappeared from the Yangtze River leaving the Yangtze finless porpoise, the only freshwater porpoise, as the sole cetacean there.

Three dolphin species live in both salt- and freshwater habitats. The Irrawaddy dolphin in South and Southeast Asia has three exclusively freshwater populations numbering fewer than 100 individuals each, whereas somewhat larger populations of thousands of individuals occur in estuaries and coastal marine waters. Two species of *Sotalia* (tucuxi and Guiana dolphins) inhabit the coastal waters from Brazil to Nicaragua as well as the Amazon. River systems and coastal areas are home to large human populations and the most intense industrial and agricultural developments, causing tremendous pressures on those habitats and the other species that live there (see Chapter 8).

WHERE THE WHALES ARE – ECOLOGICAL ZONES

The oceans are made up of dynamic and heterogeneous environments with different physical and biological characteristics. This marine realm can be divided into ecological zones characterized by water depth and distance to land. The intertidal zone, or littoral zone, falls dry at low tide and is submerged at high tide; it includes sand banks, mudflats, salt marshes and mangrove swamps. Although not usually cetacean habitat, this zone is important as a breeding ground for many fish and other prey species. Some dolphin populations have learnt to exploit this interface between the terrestrial and marine realms. Bottlenose dolphins in Florida, USA, chase mullets (small schooling fish) onto mudflats and slip up the mud after them to feast on

BELOW A killer whale beaches itself to capture a sea lion on a beach at Peninsula Valdes, Argentina.

the panicked fish. Killer whales at Peninsula Valdes, Argentina, intentionally and skilfully beach themselves when targeting large amphibious prey such as sea lions and elephant seals that are on the beach or moving between land and sea. Only certain groups of killer whales exhibit this risky behaviour, and females have to teach their young the required manoeuvres over many years. This is one of the examples of social learning and different cultural traditions in whales and dolphins (see Chapter 6).

Whales can get trapped in intertidal areas and strand. For example, Farewell Spit, a large sandbank mudflat area on the north-western tip of New Zealand's South Island, has become notorious for regular mass strandings of pilot whales. The reasons why whales strand are diverse and poorly understood (see page 53). The Farewell Spit strandings seem to be related to the local topography, with seasonally migrating pilot whales becoming disoriented in unfamiliar shallow waters. Pilot whales have strong social bonds, leading to the entire group becoming stranded, with individual whales unwilling to leave marooned or injured group members.

The second ecological zone, the continental shelf (or sublittoral zone), encompasses the shallow coastal waters from the low tide line to around 200 m (660 ft) depth. The continental shelf usually slopes gently offshore to the shelf edge, where the sea floor drops away steeply towards the deep ocean bottom. The continental shelf can be tens to hundreds of kilometres wide. It is the most important ecological zone for many whales and dolphins, at least at some point in their lives. Coastal waters and shelf zones tend to be relatively productive and stable environments. Freshwater and nutrient run-offs from land, such as near river deltas, can promote primary production and support a broad range of prey.

About half of the 32 dolphin species live exclusively in coastal and shelf waters, where prey tend to be predictable at certain times and in certain places. Most continental shelf dolphins tend to live in unstable small groups of up to a dozen individuals that mix and mingle with other groups depending on social needs, often showing strong site fidelity and limited movements. Coastal dolphins get to know their home waters very well and know when and where food is available at different times of the year. The population of around 200 coastal bottlenose dolphins off the east coast of Scotland is a good example. Some individuals reside mostly in the Moray Firth while others range more widely southwards alongshore and spend the summer months in St Andrews Bay and the Firth of Forth, probably to exploit the seasonal occurrence of prey such as salmon or mackerel.

The current distribution patterns of some closely related species cannot be explained by ecological needs alone. For example, four closely related small-bodied dolphin species in the genus *Cephalorhynchus* only occur in the continental shelf waters of southern Africa (Heaviside's dolphins), New Zealand (New Zealand and Maui's dolphins), and southern South America (Chilean and Commerson's dolphins). How did they get to inhabit such disparate continental shores separated by thousands of kilometres of the roughest and deepest oceans?

Genetic studies (see page 16) suggest that the founder population for all four species originated off southern Africa. In subsequent, stepwise dispersal events some ancestral dolphins managed to cross the open oceanic 'barrier' to reach New Zealand and colonize its island shores. In a second long-range dispersal event from New Zealand, some ancestral dolphins continued to follow the prevailing westerly winds and currents (known as the West Wind Drift) and reached South America (see page 38). Most coastal species might generally be described as 'home bodies' with limited movements, but rare long-range dispersal events can have big effects on the overall distribution patterns of species. Thus, current distribution patterns should be considered not only in light of existing ecological conditions but also as a legacy of evolutionary history and unusual past events.

Killer whales provide another intriguing example of evolutionary, ecological and social effects influencing distribution patterns. As a species, killer whales are cosmopolitan but they form distinct populations in different parts of the world with specific distribution patterns and behaviours. During the summer months Bigg's (transient) killer whales and the so-called resident killer whales both inhabit continental shelf waters off northwest North America. Bigg's killer whales specialize in hunting marine mammals, whereas resident killer whales feed on fish, primarily Chinook salmon (see page 88). A third type of killer whale occurs in the same general region but towards deeper water, and is fittingly called 'offshore'. A lot less is known about these offshore

RIGHT AND BELOW Proposed southern African origin for *Cephalorhynchus* dolphins and their subsequent dispersal along the West Wind Drift, which is thought to have led to the current distribution pattern of the four coastal species: Heaviside's dolphins (a) off southern Africa; Maui's and New Zealand dolphins (b) off New Zealand; Chilean dolphins (c) off Chile, and Commerson's dolphins (d) off eastern South America and the Kerguelen Islands.

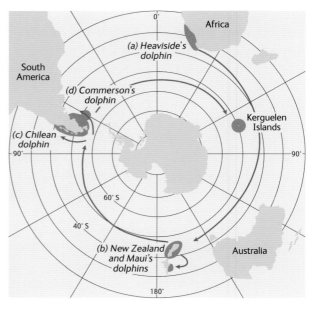

killer whales, illustrating the general bias in observation efforts to focus on nearshore shelf waters, owing to the logistic and financial constraints of conducting cetacean research at sea. Recent genetics studies suggest that strong cultural traditions (see Chapter 6) in some populations and occasional large-scale dispersal events influenced current killer whale distribution patterns. Bigg's killer whales from the North Pacific are only distantly related to the resident killer whales with which they share the coastal waters, and instead are more closely related to killer whales in the Antarctic, some 14,000 km (8,700 miles) away (see page 16).

Killer whales in Antarctica differ from each other in their coloration patterns, size, distribution and prey preferences. One type of Antarctic killer whale (unimaginatively called type B) resides in continental shelf waters along the Antarctic Peninsula, where it hunts seals. Recent tagging studies (i.e. in which a miniature computer with a satellite connection for data transmission is attached to the back of the whale – see page 64) have revealed that some type B killer whales occasionally leave Antarctica and undertake quick round-trips to the continental slope waters off Brazil. One whale swam 9,200 km (5,700 miles) in 42 days. None of the tagged whales stopped or visited known seal haul-outs along the way, so the trips were unlikely to be prey-motivated.

BELOW The killer whale is a cosmopolitan species that shows substantial morphological differences among populations.

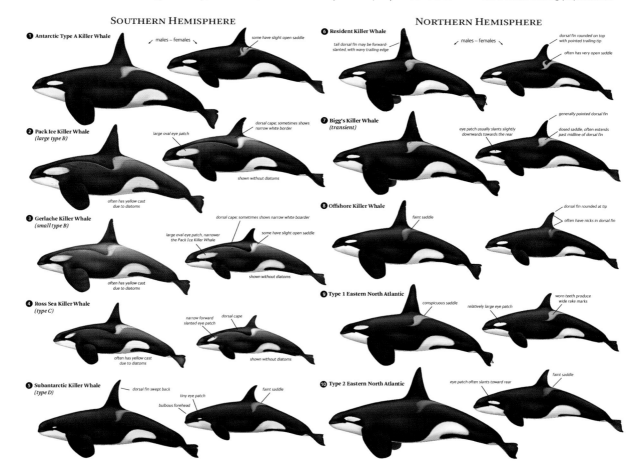

SOUTHERN HEMISPHERE   **NORTHERN HEMISPHERE**

① Antarctic Type A Killer Whale
② Pack Ice Killer Whale (large type B)
③ Gerlache Killer Whale (small type B)
④ Ross Sea Killer Whale (type C)
⑤ Subantarctic Killer Whale (type D)

⑥ Resident Killer Whale
⑦ Bigg's Killer Whale (transient)
⑧ Offshore Killer Whale
⑨ Type 1 Eastern North Atlantic
⑩ Type 2 Eastern North Atlantic

Waters off Brazil are about 25°C (45°F) warmer than Antarctic waters and it seems likely that killer whales might visit these tropical waters to maintain a healthy skin. Such physiological maintenance processes require a minimum temperature at the skin's surface for the body's enzymes to work. As the whales cannot easily warm up their skin enough in the cold Antarctic waters, they take a dash to the distant Brazilian 'sea spa'.

Thus, whale habitats are not only influenced by the availability of food or mates, but also by routine physiological needs.

Many large whale species undertake seasonal long-distance migrations (see page 60) that easily exceed the distances reported for the killer whale 'spa' trip. Migration routes of gray and humpback whales often closely follow the coastline, and scientists make use of the whales' coast-hugging behaviour to count them as they migrate past. Trained observers spend many daylight hours peering out to sea from different vantage points dotted along the coast. Such dedicated effort can help to estimate how many whales use a particular area. In some circumstances, such as the southbound migration of eastern North Pacific gray whales passing close to the coast near Carmel, California, these land-based counts have been used to estimate overall population size. This requires the use of methods that account for whales missed during the counting period because

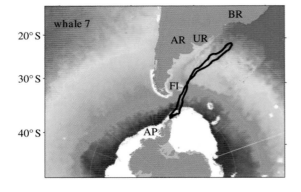

ABOVE Antarctic killer whales make rapid, directed round-trips from cool Antarctic waters (shown in blue) to warm tropical waters off Brazil (shown in red). The black line is the track of a single whale instrumented with a satellite tag.

RIGHT A gray whale swims close to shore in Magdalena Bay, Baja California, Mexico, during its annual migration.

they are migrating during the night or too far offshore to be seen from land. In winter, humpback whales, right whales and gray whales gather in shallow areas off oceanic islands or continental shores in the temperate or tropical regions to give birth to their calves or to mate. These areas are thought to afford better protection to the vulnerable calves from attacks by predators such as great white sharks or killer whales. Shallow nearshore waters also offer some protection from wind and waves (see page 60).

The third ecological zone, the continental slope, or bathyal zone, constitutes an important transition area between relatively shallow continental shelf waters and the deep ocean plains. Here, the sea floor drops away steeply from around 200 m (660 ft) to 1,000 m (0.6 miles) or more. Species inhabiting the continental slope and waters beyond are described as oceanic. In some parts of the planet the continental slope is situated relatively close to land, which helps to create special oceanographic conditions that give rise to highly productive systems. In these so-called coastal upwelling areas, the effects of ocean currents, surface winds and the slope of the ocean floor combine to force cold, nutrient-rich waters from the depths to the surface. When nutrients and light combine in the upper water column, ideal conditions are created for blooms of phytoplankton, which in turn provide ample food for zooplankton and then higher predators. Some of the most productive marine systems in the world arise from coastal upwelling, including the Peruvian-Chilean (Humboldt) Current, the California Current and Benguela Current upwelling systems.

Whales do not feed on phytoplankton but target prey higher up the food web. So there is a time lag between the occurrence of upwelling conditions, phytoplankton

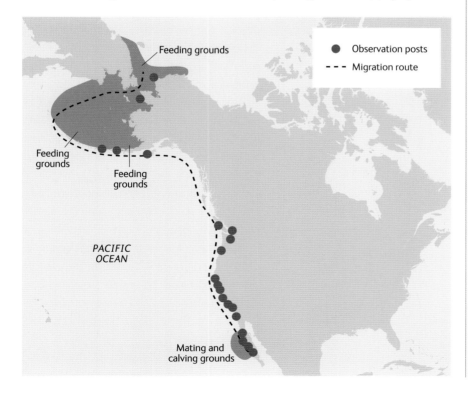

LEFT Eastern North Pacific gray whales breed, feed and migrate in continental shelf waters allowing them to be counted from observation posts on land throughout their range.

RIGHT Global current patterns (red and blue arrows) and upwelling areas (in purple). Note that upwelling areas are located mostly along coastlines and over the continental shelf and slope.

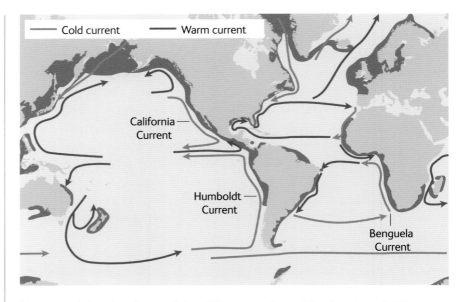

BELOW From wind to whales. Upwelling increases the primary production off the California coast during spring and early summer which leads to an increase in the number of whales using this area in late summer to autumn.

blooms and the abundance of the different predators. This 'wind-to-whale' process has been well documented for blue and fin whales, the largest predators on the planet. These whales require large aggregations of their zooplankton prey for efficient feeding, and the whales' distribution can be linked to the occurrence of highly productive marine ecosystems. We return to this in the context of migration on page 60.

Volcanic islands or sea mounts that rise steeply like isolated pinnacles from the deep ocean floor can also produce localized upwelling systems. They attract many different cetacean species, which exploit the varied ecological zones and oceanographic conditions created over very small spatial scales. Madeira, the Azores and the Canary Islands in the North Atlantic are good examples of such island hotspots surrounded by deep open ocean. Within relatively short distances from shore it is possible to observe deep diving sperm, pilot and beaked whales foraging along the narrow continental slope, and oceanic dolphins such as common or striped dolphins sometimes form temporary mixed species associations with more coastal bottlenose dolphins. Blue, fin and humpback whales are seasonal visitors, stopping by these island oases during their long-range migrations.

By far the largest part of the oceanic realm is made up of the deep open ocean

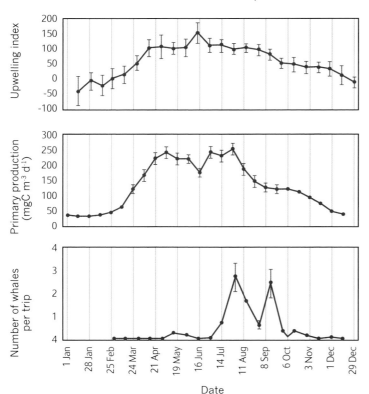

(abyssal-oceanic zone) – the fourth marine ecological zone. Although only the truly deep-diving species such as sperm, beaked and pilot whales manage to make a living in the dark and inhospitable deep ocean (see Chapters 4 and 5), many dolphin species inhabit the oceanic surface waters. This open ocean environment is generally characterized by relatively low primary productivity, with variable food patches influenced by ocean currents and surface winds. It is akin to an oceanic desert speckled with less predictable but highly profitable oases. Thus, in contrast to continental shelf species, oceanic dolphins usually roam far, swim fast and occur in large schools of hundreds to thousands of individuals to locate and exploit patches of high prey density.

In some oceanic areas, different water masses or current systems converge, giving rise to a dynamic range of oceanographic conditions defined by different physical (e.g. water temperature, oxygen content, salinity) and biological (e.g. nutrient content) characteristics. The proximity and mixing of such diverse water masses enable different species to coexist and exploit different ecological niches or preferred habitats. Such conditions can lead to a large number of different species aggregating in the same geographic area. Such large species aggregations are known from oceanic waters in tropical and subtropical regions of the South Atlantic, Indian Ocean and the Eastern Tropical Pacific (ETP).

The ETP is one of the few well-studied oceanic systems with assemblages of at least 30 cetacean species, ranging from blue whales to common, spotted and spinner dolphins, and more than 50 seabird species recorded. It is also an important commercial fishing ground for tuna and other oceanic fish. At least four major water masses and five ocean current systems converge here, providing a dynamic range of different habitats. Species distributions within the ETP change seasonally depending on life history needs (e.g. breeding) and in response to temporal and spatial shifts in water masses and currents. Larger-scale climate cycles, such as the El Niño Southern

LEFT A group of oceanic common dolphins, part of a large school, surfaces close to the volcanic Pico Island, Azores.

Oscillation (ENSO), greatly affect water temperature and the strength and mixing of ocean currents in this area, changing patterns in biological productivity and species distribution in their wake. For mobile species such as cetaceans this is not necessarily much of a problem, as they can move over wider ranges to search out more favourable environmental conditions.

In summary, where whales and dolphins occur in the oceans depends on the characteristics of the oceanic environment and each species' – or even population's – preference for particular habitats to survive and reproduce. Oceans are dynamic environments and cetaceans are generally mobile predators that can respond to changing conditions. Some larger whales are truly cosmopolitan, ranging across all climatic zones and several marine ecological zones. Species diversity of baleen whales is greatest in the Southern Hemisphere. The greatest diversity of dolphin species occurs in the tropical oceanic and continental shelf zones, whereas larger toothed whales (e.g. beaked whales) show greater diversity in temperate deep oceans.

RIGHT Predicted global distribution patterns for toothed whales (top panel) and baleen whales (bottom panel) based on statistical models that describe each species' preferred habitats. The colour palettes indicate the number of species predicted to occur in each 0.5˚x0.5˚ grid cell. Warmer colours indicate more species might occur in the same location. Note the different scales for toothed and baleen whales reflecting the different number of species in each group: toothed whales = 69 species, baleen whales = 14 species.

RIGHT Global coverage of dedicated sighting surveys for cetaceans using systematic transect surveys. The shading represents the number of surveys conducted in a particular region between 1975 and 2005. Only some parts of the world have received regular dedicated survey efforts.

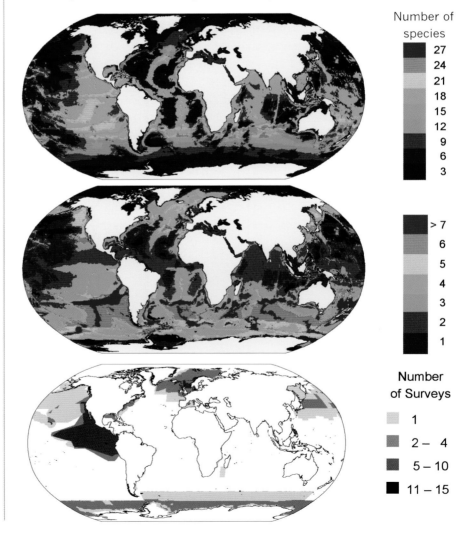

It remains a great challenge for scientists to gather relevant data to determine the distribution of whales and dolphins. Observation effort has been very patchy and highly skewed towards accessible coastal environments and developed countries with sufficient resources and legal obligations to work out where the whales are. It is also important to note that species diversity does not easily relate to the abundance of animals. How many whales there are is an even harder question to answer.

HOW MANY WHALES ARE THERE?

The short answer to the question of how many whales there are is that, for the large majority of species, we don't know. Counting cetaceans on a global scale is mission impossible. However, there are good estimates of abundance for some species, estimated using mark–recapture methods applied to photo-identification data (see box below and on page 55) or using line transect sampling methods (see box on page 47). The general picture is that some species are abundant whereas others have been reduced to very small numbers. For example, there are an estimated half a million Antarctic minke whales in the Southern Ocean and around 150,000 common minke whales in the North Atlantic. Of the smaller cetaceans, the estimated abundance of harbour porpoises approaches half a million animals in European Atlantic waters alone (see also pages 48–49). Some oceanic dolphin species are

MARK–RECAPTURE ESTIMATION OF POPULATION SIZE

A common method of estimating how many animals use a particular area over a period of time, from weeks to years, is to use mark–recapture methods. In its simplest application, mark–recapture involves a sample of animals being captured (using, for example, an array of live traps for small terrestrial mammals) and marked in some way (e.g. by applying a paint marking, a leg band or an ear tag) and released. Then, having given the animals a chance to redistribute and mix freely across their habitat, a second sample is captured and numbers of marked and unmarked animals are recorded. The proportion of animals in the second sample that were previously marked should, if a number of assumptions are met, equal the proportion of marked animals in the whole population. These data can easily be used to estimate population size. Most studies use many sampling occasions to build up more extensive data sets; this allows more complex analysis and ultimately more robust estimation of population size.

We can use the same approach with whales and dolphins. Individuals of many species have unique natural markings (e.g. nicks and notches on the dorsal fin of a dolphin or a particular coloration pattern on a whale) and good-quality photographs of these can be used to 'capture'

and 'mark' animals instead of physically capturing them and applying artificial marks (see page 55). Individuals captured by photo-identification are compared to those already stored in a specially created identification catalogue to determine whether they are recaptures or a newly captured animal.

Mark–recapture methods have been successfully applied to photo-identification data sets from many cetacean species, from bottlenose dolphins to blue whales, all over the world. In some species, not all individuals bear distinguishing natural markings; for example, dolphins typically acquire nicks/notches on their dorsal fins as they age so young animals may be unmarked. In these cases, the mark–recapture estimates will only pertain to the number of individuals in the population that do have recognizable marks. We can calculate the proportion of animals in the population that do possess markings and scale the mark–recapture estimate to the total population size. Mark–recapture methods work especially well for coastal species, and are the main approach used to estimate the size of local dolphin populations or the number of whales in discrete breeding or feeding areas.

widespread geographically and number in the hundreds of thousands. At the other extreme, Maui's dolphin in northern New Zealand and the vaquita porpoise in the upper Gulf of California, Mexico are confined to very restricted areas and have critically low numbers of fewer than 100 individuals. After the demise of the baiji in China the next cetacean species likely to go extinct in the near future is the vaquita, unless urgent effective actions are taken promptly to completely eliminate incidental catches in fishing gear (see page 124).

Researchers may have to use complex and often costly methods to estimate the number of cetaceans in geographically defined areas that are deemed of particular interest. The motivation for this 'interest' in how many whales there are in a particular area can be as diverse as the species to study. The question of 'how many whales' often goes hand in hand with the question of whether there are 'fewer or more whales than before'. Knowing how many animals there were and are now in a population or a species is core to conservation and is required to manage human activities affecting whales and entire ocean ecosystems (see Chapters 7 and 8). The International Union for Conservation of Nature (IUCN) assesses the conservation status of plant and animal species, including cetaceans, and publishes expert evaluations in the IUCN Species Red List. The main purpose of this list is to identify those species (or distinct populations) threatened with extinction and to prioritize the level of threat (Vulnerable, Endangered, Critically Endangered) to facilitate international conservation efforts. Abundance estimates, trends in abundance and changes to species' ranges are key criteria used in the assessment process.

The large rorqual (balaenopterid) species (blue, fin and sei whales) are still classified as Endangered as a result of their decimation by whaling in the 20th century (see Chapter 7). Blue whales in the Southern Ocean are thought to have been reduced to around three per cent of their pre-whaling population sizes, with the current population estimated to number in the low thousands. Right whales in the Northern Hemisphere are substantially rarer with only around 500 individuals in the North Atlantic and probably no more in total in the North Pacific. These are critically low sizes for slow-reproducing, long-lived species (see page 51), and both species are classified as Endangered. In contrast, many previously exploited populations of humpback, gray and bowhead whales as well as Southern right whales have shown sustained population increases, leading to their removal from threatened categories to a listing of Least Concern.

One of the problems with the IUCN listings for whales is that most species have only been assessed globally but different populations in different areas may have a different conservation status. For example, gray whales are globally listed as Least Concern because the population in the eastern North Pacific has recovered to around 20,000 animals, but the population in the western North Pacific is only a few hundred and qualifies as Endangered. Work in the IUCN is ongoing to assess regional cetacean populations. However, most cetacean species are classed as Data Deficient because there is not enough information on present and past population sizes and biology to assess their status or threats to them.

LINE TRANSECT SAMPLING TO ESTIMATE ABUNDANCE

Line transect sampling is a method originally developed for surveying terrestrial species to provide estimates of the number of animals in a predefined area. In the late 1970s, researchers started to apply these methods to shipboard and aerial surveys of whales. The basic idea is that trained observers search with binoculars or the naked eye for whales from a ship or an aircraft as it travels along a set of predetermined transect lines. The strip searched on either side of the transect lines provides a sample of the whole survey area – hence the name of the method.

It is harder to detect a whale the further away it is, so the probability of detection decreases as the distance from the transect line increases; therefore, not all the whales within the strip searched will be seen. To account for the animals missed, when a whale or group of whales is detected (usually referred to as a 'sighting'), the observers collect data that allow the perpendicular distance of the whales from the

transect line to be determined (as well as data on species and the size of the group). These distances are then used to estimate the average detection probability within the defined strip. This use of perpendicular distance data leads to this method also being known as distance sampling. Once the average detection probability within the strip searched has been estimated, the sample density of whales can be calculated and then extrapolated to the whole survey area to provide an estimate of total abundance within that area.

One important feature of the line transect sampling method is the assumption that all animals are seen directly ahead on the transect line. This clearly is not the case for most cetaceans, which spend the majority of their lives underwater. In addition, some species, for example common dolphins, may respond to an approaching ship by swimming towards it while others, for example harbour porpoises and minke whales, may respond by moving away before being detected. Missing animals on the transect line and undetected responsive movement are both problematic in surveys for cetaceans and can lead to serious over- or underestimation of abundance depending on the species. To address these problems, an extension of the method can be employed, in which a second team of observers collect independent data. These data are then used to estimate the proportion of sightings missed by one team or the other (in a manner similar to the mark–recapture method: see box on page 45) and also, if necessary, to correct for responsive movement.

Surveys are conducted during a defined time period, typically when the weather and sea conditions are favourable for visual observations. Thus, line transect (distance) sampling gives a snapshot of the number of whales in a given area at a particular point in time, usually summer.

LEFT Two teams of observers searching for whales during the SCANS-III ship-board survey in the Bay of Biscay, northern Spain in July 2016.

Population assessments are often triggered by an emerging conservation crisis or pressure to exploit marine resources in a more sustainable commercial or ecological manner. Cetaceans in the ETP have become some of the longest and best studied oceanic species because of the very large numbers of dolphins killed as bycatch in highly valued fisheries for yellowfin tuna (see pages 124–125). As a result, a programme of large-scale systematic line transect surveys (see box above) was established by the US government to estimate abundance and determine population status of the ETP dolphins. Results of these surveys and back-calculations to estimate historical numbers

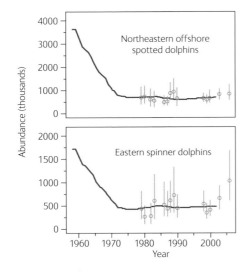

show that these dolphin populations declined sharply from several million animals to hundreds of thousands during the 1960s and early 1970s. Although these surveys have enabled a much better understanding of this complex ecosystem, it is still unknown why the dolphin populations have shown limited signs of recovery since mortalities were greatly reduced from the early 1970s onwards.

Large-scale abundance surveys are expensive, labour-intensive, and weather dependent, and provide only brief snapshots of the cetacean populations in the area of interest. Few places in the world have been studied sufficiently regularly and intensively to allow for trends in population size and species distribution to be investigated over time. Large-scale systematic surveys, driven in part by the need to assess the impact of fisheries bycatch (see page 124) have been conducted in the North Sea, and continental shelf and offshore waters of the European

PASSIVE ACOUSTIC SURVEY

Not all whales are easy to see, but most whales can be heard. This means that whales can be studied when they are out of sight underwater, when the light conditions do not allow for visual observations (e.g. at night) or when the weather conditions are too rough for visual observations from ships or aircraft. Passive acoustic surveys rely on species-specific vocalization characteristics to distinguish whale sounds from background noise and to identify different species. Porpoises, sperm whales, beaked whales and most baleen whales have distinct vocalizations that allow species identity to be established. Species discrimination is less well developed for most dolphins, because their vocalizations are either too poorly known or are too similar between species. This is an active field of research, and novel methods are being developed.

Mobile passive acoustic surveys involve towing one or more hydrophones (underwater microphones) behind

a ship with the cable connected to a computer running acoustic detection software. Passive acoustic surveys can be conducted in tandem with visual surveys – see box on line transect sampling on page 47 – to enhance the probability of detecting cetaceans. Ship noise (e.g. from propeller cavitation) can mask cetacean vocalisations, so a 'quiet' survey vessel and a long cable towing the hydrophones far behind the ship are essential. Mobile passive acoustic surveys have focused mainly on porpoise and sperm whales but are also used for other odontocetes.

Static passive acoustic surveys involve mooring autonomous acoustic devices on the sea floor and letting them record all ambient sounds over a period of time. Sound recordings are stored on memory cards; thus, devices typically need to be recovered to access the data. A recent development is to build acoustic moorings with links to surface buoys from which data are transmitted using mobile phone or satellite connections. Software is then used to filter whale vocalizations from underwater noise and identify the calling species. Static passive acoustic surveys are often employed to detect migrating baleen whales or monitor whale activity in particular areas of interest (e.g. conservation areas or shipping channels – see page 132) or around human-made structures (e.g. fishing nets, fish farms, oil rigs). There is ongoing research to investigate ways to use such static passive acoustic data to estimate numbers of whales in an area.

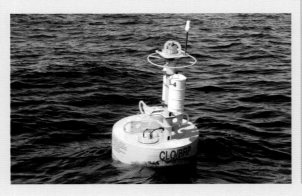

LEFT A real-time auto-detection buoy floating on the surface and transmitting data on whale calls recorded underwater.

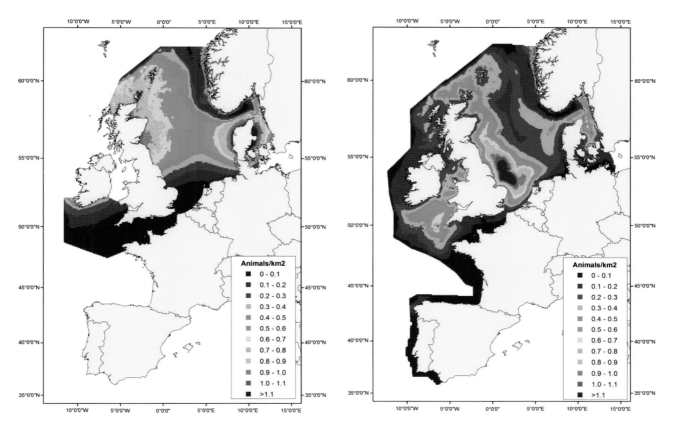

Atlantic to estimate abundance of harbour porpoises, and various dolphin and whale species. Surveys in 1994 and 2005 showed that the number of harbour porpoises had remained relatively stable but that their distribution had changed markedly. The reasons for the porpoises' distributional shift are not yet clearly understood but are most likely related to changes in the distribution of their prey.

Some cetacean species are much harder to sight than others because of their behaviour. Harbour porpoises are small, cryptic and may avoid ships. Deep-diving species such as sperm and beaked whales spend so little time at the surface that they are only available to be seen for a small proportion of the time. Therefore, other survey methods may be more appropriate for some of these species, depending on the aims of the study.

Toothed whales rely on the use of sound to navigate, detect prey and communicate (see page 25). Baleen whales also make species-specific calls, usually to communicate with conspecifics (other members of the same species) over large distances; an example of this is humpback whale song, described on pages 104–106. These vocalizations can be used to detect their presence in a particular area even when they cannot be seen. In the case of sperm whales, methods have been developed to use their characteristic echolocation clicks to obtain robust estimates of abundance. Being able to detect and even track whales and porpoises using passive acoustic listening has greatly increased our understanding of their distribution and occurrence patterns, and is helping to mitigate human effects on them (see page 132).

OPPOSITE TOP Estimated changes in abundance from 1959–2012 of the two dolphin populations most affected by tuna purse-seine fishing in the eastern tropical Pacific. Estimates of abundance between 1979 and 2006 are shown as points with 95% confidence intervals. The populations declined due to high numbers of dolphins killed in the tuna fishery in the 1960s and early 1970s, and have failed to recover since this mortality was progressively reduced.

ABOVE LEFT AND RIGHT Predicted density of harbour porpoises from the SCANS and SCANS-II surveys in 1994 (left) and 2005 (right). The warmer colours show areas of higher density, which have shifted southwards into the southern North Sea. A third survey (SCANS-III) in 2016 showed that this pattern has persisted.

CHAPTER 3

The circle of life

L IKE ALL OTHER ANIMALS, whales must use the energy they obtain from feeding to grow, to survive and ultimately to reproduce. How successfully they can do this is a measure of their 'fitness'. The fitter the individual, the more healthy young they will produce over their lifetime and the more their offspring will contribute to future generations. The differential success of individuals surviving and reproducing drives the evolutionary process of natural selection, first described by Charles Darwin in his book *On the Origin of Species* published in 1859.

The way in which animals organize their lives to obtain food and to allocate energy from that food to grow, survive and reproduce is known as their life history: literally, the story of how they lead their lives at a timescale relevant to the biology of the species. Whales are large-bodied, long-lived animals that give birth infrequently, meaning that the pace of their life history is very slow compared with that of most other species. Species with slow life histories have adapted to live in stable environments in which food and other resources, such as mates, are predictably available. For whales, the oceans provide such a stable environment.

The slow life histories of whales are characterized by several features. Adult whales have high survival rates (i.e. low rates of natural mortality) leading to life spans of several decades. Young whales spend a number of years as juveniles before they reach maturity and are able to reproduce. Each female has to invest a lot of time and energy to produce a calf, so a mother typically gives birth no more frequently than every two or three years, always to a single calf; she thus produces relatively few calves during her lifetime. A mother's care of her offspring after birth means that calves also have high survival rates – but not as high as mature animals.

Does this sound familiar? It may do because the life histories of whales are in many respects very similar to those of humans. Other marine predators such as seals and some seabirds also have slow life histories for the same reasons as whales – a response to the stable environments in which they live.

Species such as whales that have evolved slow life histories in predictable environments are sometimes described as 'K-selected' species because their life histories lead to stable populations at levels that are limited by the amount of resources in the environment (the carrying capacity, denoted 'K'). In contrast,

OPPOSITE North Atlantic right whale mother and calf swimming closely together. Right and bowhead whales are the longest lived cetaceans and reproduce no more frequently than every three years.

species that live in unpredictable environments tend to have 'r-selected' life histories in which there is a premium on being able to reproduce rapidly ('r' is the reproductive rate) to take advantage of good conditions when they occur.

The slow 'K-selected' life history that is characteristic of whales may be a successful evolutionary strategy in stable, predictable oceanic environments, but it means that whales may be ill equipped to cope with interactions with humans because of their inability to reproduce, and therefore recover, quickly. Any human activity that leads to an increase in mortality, deliberate or accidental, may therefore have severe negative impacts on whale populations. The most obvious example of this is past industrial-scale whaling, which reduced many whale populations to a very small fraction of their natural size, and from which recovery has taken, or is still taking, decades or longer (see Chapter 7). Other activities that affect the fitness of whales may also compromise their ability to maintain population sizes close to the levels that can be supported by the natural environment. For example, disturbance away from favoured feeding or breeding areas by wind farm construction, seismic surveys, military activity or even whale-watching could potentially lead to long-term effects on growth, survival or reproduction. Human impact on the world's oceans is high and increasing; we return to the effects of this on whale populations in Chapter 8.

AGE, LONGEVITY, SURVIVAL AND MORTALITY

Compared to most species, whales live a long time, typically for many decades, although the majority of the smaller dolphins and porpoises usually do not live as long.

Estimating the age of a whale is not straightforward. For the odontocetes (toothed whales), it is possible to count the layers of dentine in teeth that have been sectioned and stained. These layers are laid down periodically and regularly (usually annually), similar to the rings in a tree, and this method tells us that sperm whales may live for up to 70 years and pilot whales for up to 60 years. Studies of free-living killer whales identified by their natural markings began in the 1970s in British Columbia. Using estimates of the age of adult animals at the beginning of the study, it has been shown that female killer whales can live for up to 90 years and males for up to 60 years.

RIGHT This sperm whale tooth has been sectioned to reveal its growth layers.

Mysticetes (baleen whales) do not have teeth, but some species can be aged by examining plugs from the external ear, which consist of waxy layers deposited regularly in an annual pattern. These ear plugs are not made of true wax but of skin cells transformed into a tough composite of keratin in a crystalline cholesterol matrix. Analysis of ear plugs extracted from whales killed in whaling operations has shown that fin and blue whales may live for up to 90–100 years, and humpback and minke whales for up to 40–50 years.

A biochemical method first developed in the 1960s to assess the age of marine sediments has been used to estimate the age of some whales. The method is based on a process called racemization, in which one form of aspartic acid (an amino acid used in the making of proteins) slowly converts into another form at a predictable rate. The best animal tissue to use for analysis has been found to be the nucleus of the eye lens. Using eye lenses from narwhal and bowhead whales hunted by Inuit off West Greenland and Alaska, respectively, the aspartic acid racemization method indicates that narwhals may live to more than 100 years and that bowhead whales may live to more than 200 years. The remarkable discovery of a 115–130-year-old Yankee whaling harpoon embedded in a bowhead whale taken by Inuit hunters in Alaska supports the finding that bowheads can live for well over 100 years.

The smaller odontocetes do not live so long. Depending on the species, dolphins may typically live to around 20–30 years, but some species are known to live longer. One female bottlenose dolphin in Sarasota Bay, Florida was known to be 66 years old in 2016. One of the smallest cetaceans, the harbour porpoise, typically lives for only about 10 years and rarely more than 20 years.

Most of what we know about the natural causes of death of cetaceans comes from post-mortem examination of carcasses, many of which are of stranded animals. Natural causes of death include infectious disease and parasite infection, both of which can cause pneumonia and starvation. Because whales are so long-lived, some may eventually simply die of old age. In strandings of many live animals, so-called mass strandings in which animals are typically otherwise apparently healthy, the act of beaching may itself be the cause of death, but the large majority of strandings are of single animals that are already dead.

There are several theories for natural causes of mass strandings, including atypical behaviour of following prey into waters very close to the shore, tight-knit social groups following a diseased or disorientated animal into the shallows, and navigation errors caused by magnetic anomalies in certain areas. In most cases the root cause is undetermined. Mortality caused by or linked to human activities, such as entanglement in fishing gear, being struck by a ship or being incapacitated by noise, is covered in Chapter 8.

The maximum lifespan is not the only way to consider how long an animal may live. Another measure is life expectancy: how long a whale is expected to live on average. The mortality rate of young animals is higher than that of adults and it is also higher for very old animals as they reach the end of their natural life. If you plot

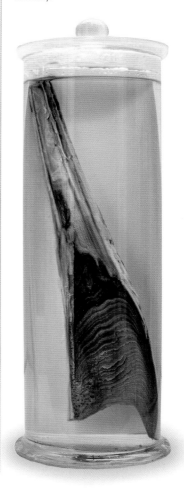

BELOW An ear plug from a fin whale showing the waxy layers deposited annually.

ABOVE A mass stranding of 26 pilot whales that occurred at Pittenweem in eastern Scotland on 2 September 2012; ten animals were 'refloated' alive and survived.

BELOW A typical mammalian U-shaped age-specific mortality curve derived from data from stranded male bottlenose dolphins in the Indian River Lagoon, Florida, USA.

mortality rate against age, therefore, you will see a U-shaped curve that is typical of the mortality schedule of a long-lived K-selected species with a slow life history.

Because mortality rate is not constant throughout the life of a whale, life expectancy is also specific to age. The life expectancy of a newborn calf is relatively short because the chances of it dying before reaching adulthood, when mortality rates become very low, are relatively high. But as the calf gets older, its life expectancy increases for a few years. For example, data from a study of stranded bottlenose dolphins in the Indian River Lagoon, Florida, USA show that the life expectancy of females rises from 12 years at birth to 16 years at 5 years of age. The equivalent figures for males are 9 and 11 years. Life expectancy then declines steadily from 5 years of age. The maximum age in these animals was 35 years.

This illustrates an obvious but important point: only a tiny percentage of the population will live to the maximum age; the large majority of animals will live much shorter lives. This means that the average age of the animals in a population is younger than might be expected. For Indian River Lagoon bottlenose dolphins, the average ages of females and males in the population were only 11 and 8 years, respectively. What happens to a whale after it dies at sea is described on pages 96–97.

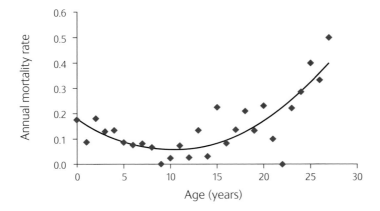

STUDYING WHALES USING PHOTO-IDENTIFICATION

In the 1960s and 1970s, researchers began using the ability to recognize different whales or dolphins from their natural markings to study the lives of individuals by taking pictures of them – a method called photo-identification. Some of these original studies have become established long-term programmes of research that have led to greatly improved knowledge about movements, behaviour, population size, survival and birth rates. Such studies include those of bottlenose dolphins in Sarasota Bay, Florida, killer whales off British Columbia and Washington State, right whales off Argentina, blue whales in the Gulf of St Lawrence, Canada and humpback whales across the North Atlantic. There are now many photo-identification studies around the world investigating a wide range of cetacean species.

The markings used to identify individuals depend on the species. Bottlenose and other dolphins are identified from nicks and notches in the trailing edge of their dorsal fin (see page 59). Killer whales are similarly recognized but also from the shape of the gray saddle patch behind the fin. Identification of individual right whales relies on the pattern of callosities (hardened skin inhabited by whale lice and barnacles) on their heads, for blue whales it is from the pattern of pigmentation on their flanks and for humpback whales it is from the coloration and trailing edge of their tail flukes.

Much of what we know about these and other species has come from long-term photo-identification studies. The longer these studies continue the more our knowledge will improve.

BELOW Illustrations of the natural markings used to identify individual whales of various species: right whale (top left); humpback whale (bottom left); killer whale (top right); blue whale (bottom right).

THE LIFE CYCLE

The sequence of events from the birth of an animal to when it dies is known as the life cycle. A newborn whale calf is fed and cared for by its mother, gains independence when it is weaned, grows and develops further as a juvenile until reaching maturity, reproduces as an adult and eventually grows old and dies. However, because of natural mortality, some animals never survive long enough to breed. About 80 per cent of female killer whales off British Columbia and Washington State survive to have a calf of their own, but in Indian River Lagoon bottlenose dolphins, only around half of newborn animals make it as far as maturity.

SEXUAL MATURITY

The process of reproduction is initiated by the onset of sexual maturity. The age at which a young whale becomes mature varies widely among the different whale species. Some humpback whales in the Gulf of Maine are known to have become sexually mature by the age of 4 years. In killer whales, age at sexual maturity may be anything from 6 to 15 years. In long living bowhead whales in the Arctic, it is around 25 years.

In some species, becoming sexually mature does not guarantee breeding. Sperm whale females begin having calves at around 10 years of age. Males take much longer to develop and do not reach sexual maturity until about 20 years, and even then it may be several more years before an individual is socially mature and able to outcompete other males and mate.

The age at which an individual whale reaches sexual maturity depends to some extent on the quantity of food resources it has managed to consume early in life. The more food available, the sooner it may become mature, because well-nourished animals develop quicker. This may occur because of natural variation in the availability of prey, but another reason could be because a reduction in population size from the natural carrying capacity (the population size able to be supported by the environment) has made more food available per whale. Reaching maturity at a younger age may thus be a response to reduced whale density and acts to increase reproduction so that the population recovers more quickly to the natural carrying capacity. Such a mechanism is known as a density dependent response. The decline in the age at sexual maturity in female fin whales in the Southern Ocean from around 10 years in whales born in the 1910s and 1920s to around 6 years in whales born in the 1940s and 1950s is believed to be a density-dependent response to the massive reduction in the population of fin whales in the 1930s due to whaling (see page 114).

REPRODUCTIVE SENESCENCE AND LIFETIME OUTPUT

How many offspring a female is able to have over her lifetime depends partly on how long she can continue to reproduce. In most animal species, reproduction continues until death, but females of some mammals may stop reproducing before the end of their lives. This is particularly known to occur in primates but is also found in seals and other carnivores, deer, sheep, horses, elephants and even rodents; it has also been shown in seabirds. However, a pattern in which most females stop reproducing for about one-third of their lifespan, equivalent to the menopause in humans, is far less common. The best evidence of a menopause in cetaceans comes from pilot whales and killer whales. Female short-finned pilot whales in the North Pacific and long-finned pilot whales in the North Atlantic may live to at least 60 years, but pregnancies after the age of 40 are very rare. Killer whale females off British Columbia and Washington State are estimated to live up to 90 years, but no calves are born to females older than 50–60 years. Pilot whales and killer whales both have a type of social organization in which stable groups of whales are composed of mothers and their offspring (described as matrilineal). The most plausible explanation for the extended post-reproductive lives of females in these species is that older females that have stopped having calves nevertheless contribute to the care of offspring in some other way – the so-called 'grandmother effect'. By helping with the care of young and finding food, these older, more experienced females can contribute to the fitness of their close relatives.

Given the length of a female's reproductive lifetime – from sexual maturity to death or menopause – her lifetime reproductive output is determined by how many calves she produces in that period. The interval between the births of consecutive calves has a natural minimum because of the length of time taken by the various components of the reproductive cycle, but it may also vary depending on how much food is available to the female to build up her energy stores in advance of pregnancy and lactation (feeding her young with milk).

THE REPRODUCTIVE CYCLE

The female reproductive cycle starts with ovulation (release of an egg) and subsequent mating and fertilization by the male. Ovulation is typically seasonal and believed to be brought on by increasing daylength. In some species, such as fin and humpback whales, a female may only ovulate once in a season but in others, such

LEFT A breaching Cuvier's beaked whale in the northwest Atlantic. The scars on its body are probably a result of fighting with other males.

as the pilot whale, there may be multiple ovulations. The male reproductive cycle, not surprisingly, is closely linked to that of the female. At the same time that females are ovulating, males undergo physical changes causing each testis and epididymis, where sperm are stored, to enlarge and thus produce and store more sperm.

In right whales, the weight of both testes during the breeding season may be as large as a staggering one tonne (just over one ton), around one per cent of the animal's total weight. This incomparable size is believed to be the result of sperm competition during mating; many males mate with a female, so the male that can produce the most sperm is most likely to fertilize the egg and be the father of her calf. In some species, there are pronounced behavioural changes, which may involve aggression among competing males; males in these species may bear the scars of such fighting. Male humpback whales 'sing' to attract females and may 'escort' females that are in oestrus (ready to mate) to ensure copulating opportunities when she is receptive. How different versions of these songs spread across the South Pacific Ocean over periods of years is described on pages 104–106.

After conception, a pregnant whale will carry her calf for approximately a year, although this varies among species, from 10–11 months in most dolphins and porpoises to as long as 15–17 months in larger odontocetes: pilot whales, killer whales, belugas, narwhals and sperm whales. In baleen whales, gestation is typically 11–12 months but is only 10 months in minke whales and may be as long as 14 months in gray whales and bowhead whales. Whale foetuses grow rapidly, and their weight increases at an exponentially increasing rate throughout pregnancy. Just before its birth, a blue whale foetus is increasing in weight by about 35 kg (5½ stones) per day.

Parturition (birth) occurs at full term and is very quick, as one might expect for air-breathing animals born underwater. Odontocetes are typically born tail first but mysticetes may be born head or tail first. A newborn calf is one-quarter to one-third of the length of its mother. This very large size illustrates well the extent of parental investment during pregnancy. Some migratory baleen whales give birth in particular

BELOW A bottlenose dolphin giving birth in captivity – note that the calf is born tail-first.

areas in warm tropical waters (see pages 60–62). The non-migratory toothed whales, dolphins and porpoises are not known to have specific calving areas.

Mothers assist their newborn calves to reach the surface to breathe. Then the female will spend a period of months to years suckling her calf on energy-rich milk containing up to almost 50 per cent fat. Mysticete lactation lasts for several months, but in most species of odontocete a calf will not be weaned for several years. In bottlenose dolphins, for example, a calf will usually stay with its mother for three years before becoming independent. In killer whales this period may extend for several more years. Remarkably, a 13-year-old sperm whale has been found with milk in its stomach. These extended lactation periods are also a good illustration of the high parental investment in cetaceans.

After the calf is weaned and independent, it is usual for the mother to spend a period resting; reproduction is very demanding for a female and she needs this time to replenish her energy resources before embarking on another pregnancy. The length of this resting period can be as short as about six months in some migratory baleen whales (see page 61) and up to several years in the toothed whales. Thus, the complete reproductive cycle typically takes a minimum of two to three years in baleen whales and longer in toothed whales.

CLOCKWISE FROM TOP LEFT
A female bottlenose dolphin (note the distinguishing nick in her dorsal fin) with her calf from the east coast of Scotland, when the calf was new born (top left), 1 year old (bottom left), 2 years old (top right) and 3 years old (bottom right).

Two notable species are exceptions to the rule. Minke whales and harbour porpoises generally breed every year and therefore have an annual reproductive cycle. Females of these two species are thus pregnant almost constantly and are also lactating for several months of this time. Being both pregnant and lactating is unusual in mammals, because the hormones produced during lactation act to suppress conception. The energy resources required to carry a foetus for almost a year whilst simultaneously feeding a newborn calf for several months make minke whale and harbour porpoise mothers quite remarkable in the cetacean world.

MIGRATION

Several species of baleen whale make long annual migrations from high latitude feeding areas in summer to low latitude breeding (mating and calving) areas in winter. This seasonal migration is an integral part of the life cycle of these whales and has a major influence on the reproductive cycle. A driving factor of this migration is the seasonal variation in abundance of food in cooler waters.

Every spring in high latitudes, increasing temperatures lead to stratification of the ocean water column into an uppermost layer, into which sunlight can penetrate (called the photic zone), and a deeper layer into which it cannot (called the aphotic zone). The increasing daylight and accumulated nutrients in the photic zone allow phytoplankton (microscopic aquatic plants) to photosynthesize and reproduce very rapidly, resulting in the 'spring bloom'. Zooplankton, including krill, feeding on the phytoplankton also increase but with a time lag and less rapidly because they are slower growing. Predators feeding on zooplankton, including fish, then also increase. By summer, the cool temperate and sub-polar waters of the northern Atlantic, northern Pacific and Southern Ocean provide a rich source of food for organisms further up the food chain, such as larger fish, squid, seabirds and marine mammals.

In autumn, cooling temperatures and an increase in turbulence due to stronger winds break up the stratification through vertical mixing of the water column. This mixing means that phytoplankton are no longer able to stay near the surface, their mortality increases and the decreased daylight leads to declining photosynthesis and reproduction. During winter these waters thus have very much lower prey availability than in the summer and they hold less attraction for whales and other predators.

Waters in lower latitudes are also not rich in prey, but they are warmer, have better visibility and may be more sheltered than in higher latitudes and thus may be more suitable for a female to give birth and for a calf to survive the first few weeks of life; this may be part of the reason why baleen whales migrate.

In fact, several explanations have been proposed for baleen whale migration, a question that has generated considerable debate. These include the idea that it is energetically more efficient for whales to swim to warmer waters than to overwinter in cold waters; that whales move towards the equator in winter to find food that is lacking in high latitude waters; that calves survive and grow better in warmer,

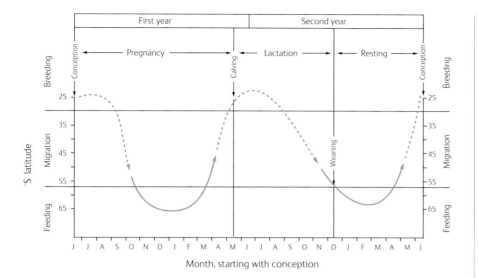

LEFT Schematic representation of the migration pattern and reproductive cycle of a female fin whale in the Southern Hemisphere.

calmer waters; and that there is a reduced risk of killer whale predation on calves in tropical waters. There is more support for some of these ideas than others and, in any case, there is unlikely to be a 'one-size-fits-all' explanation for migration because of differences in behaviour among the various migrating species.

Whatever the reason or reasons, the extreme migrations of some baleen whales of thousands of kilometres each way each year between feeding and breeding areas are remarkable. Humpback whales may swim 8,000 km (5,000 miles) each way during their annual migration, but a female gray whale in the North Pacific is the current record holder, having swum from her feeding area off Russia to the breeding lagoons of Baja California, Mexico and back again in less than six months – a round trip of 22,500 km (14,000 miles).

To illustrate how the reproductive cycle of a baleen whale is integrated with its migratory behaviour, consider the life of a typical female Southern Hemisphere fin whale. Ovulation, mating and fertilization occur in June in low latitudes. Gestation lasts 11 months, during which time she migrates southwards to feed in rich Antarctic waters between October and March/April. She then migrates northwards again to give birth in May in low latitudes. Lactation lasts seven months, during which time she migrates poleward again while feeding her calf until they arrive in the Southern Ocean in December of this second year. Her calf is now weaned and will feed independently, while she feeds and recovers before migrating northwards again to breed. The whole cycle thus takes two years.

Another species that has a well-documented migratory reproductive cycle is the humpback whale in the North Atlantic. This whale undertakes a similar migration to that of the fin whale but lagged by six months because of the difference in seasons between the hemispheres. Unlike fin whales, we do know where humpback whales breed. During the period of intensive commercial whaling (see Chapter 7), humpbacks were taken in breeding areas around the Cape Verde Islands off the coast of Africa and also in the West Indies. Today, very few whales breed in the eastern Atlantic, and their major breeding area is on Silver Bank north of the Dominican Republic in the West Indies.

Research to investigate the populations of humpback whales in the North Atlantic has revealed that many (possibly thousands) of whales that feed in Norwegian and Icelandic waters have a different genetic signature from whales that breed in the West Indies, indicating that there is another major breeding area somewhere. It is not at the Cape Verde Islands, so where is it? We do not yet know.

In summer, humpback whales feed in distinct areas in the Gulf of Maine, along the coasts of Labrador and Newfoundland and in the Gulf of St Lawrence, Canada, off West Greenland, around Iceland, and off northern Norway, particularly around Bear Island. Although humpback whales from all of these feeding areas mix and breed together in the West Indies, each individual whale only migrates to one of the feeding areas. A calf returning with its mother to her feeding area will then also return there year after year. This maternally directed area preference means that populations of whales in each feeding area are distinct, even though they all mate together in the breeding areas.

Unlike most of the baleen whales, the toothed whales generally do not migrate. Instead, their life history is adapted to breeding in the same areas where they

BELOW Schematic of North Atlantic humpback migrations between breeding areas in the south and feeding areas in the north. The weight of the lines represents the number of animals that have been observed moving between the areas.. Only one whale has been recorded migrating between the southeast Caribbean and Scotland.

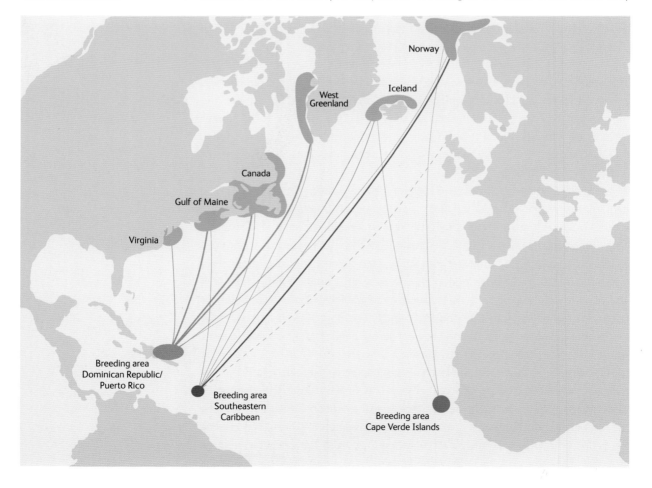

spend their lives feeding. These areas may change seasonally because of seasonal changes in prey availability, but there is no directed movement from one area to another to perform different activities. This illustrates an important difference between the reproductive strategies of the migratory baleen whales and non-migratory toothed whales. The toothed whales spend their lives where they can feed all year; they are thus 'income breeders' because they can support the energetic cost of reproduction continuously. The migratory baleen whales are 'capital breeders' because they must lay down all the energy stores needed for lactation while in the summer feeding areas and survive without food between giving birth and weaning their calves.

An exception to the non-migratory odontocetes are sperm whale males. Sperm whale females and juveniles form stable social groups and remain in tropical waters year-round, but mature males are solitary and migrate to high latitudes for much of the year, where they can take advantage of the higher productivity in these waters.

ABOVE A humpback whale and its calf in the Hawaiian Islands Humpback Whale National Marine Sanctuary.

TRACKING THE MOVEMENTS OF WHALES

Early information on the movements of whales came from Discovery tags, bolts of steel about 30 cm (12 in) long that were fired into the blubber of whales to be recovered from the butchered carcass if the whale was subsequently killed in whaling operations. This gave only two data points, so the information was very limited. Data from individual whales recognized by their unique natural markings (see the box on photo-identification on page 55) have also provided some information on movements between observations. But to track the movements of a whale in more detail, we need to attach a tag to the whale that tells us where it is at a given point in time. To provide information on large scale distribution and migratory movements, the tag needs to stay on the whale for months, and ideally for a whole annual cycle.

Keeping a tag attached to a whale is challenging. Even large, slow-swimming whales have evolved a streamlined body. Water is hundreds of times denser than air, and any external device will markedly increase drag. Tags can be attached by suction cup for short-term deployments of hours to days (see pages 68 and 85), but more invasive attachment methods are needed for longer-term attachments. These involve embedding, anchoring or pinning the tag to the animal. The blubber must be sufficiently thick that the tag can be anchored in the animal without reaching the muscle layer. Larger species of whales cannot be caught or handled, so tags

must be attached using remote launchers that can accurately place the tag in a safe part of the body with enough force to implant the anchors. For small species, such as porpoises, the animal can be captured and the tag can be pinned through the dorsal fin, which has few nerves. All these tags are designed to be expelled from or fall off the animal after a period of time, which may be weeks, months or even more than a year. (See page 68 for how the tags are deployed.)

The satellite system used to retrieve information from a tag on a whale is Service Argos, which operates on board polar-orbiting satellites. Transmissions from the tag are received by the satellites and data on the whale's location are relayed to land so that researchers can study the movements of whales wherever they go in the world. The global positioning system (GPS) provides better accuracy than Argos locations, but use of GPS requires either recovery of the data by retrieving the tag, or use of another system (such as GSM phone) to transmit the data.

The continued development and increasing deployment of these tags has increased enormously our knowledge of the movements, distribution, migration and use of particular habitats of many species of whale. The North Pacific gray whale that was recorded swimming more than 22,000 km (13,670 miles) from its feeding area to its breeding area and back again in 6 months was fitted with such a transmitter.

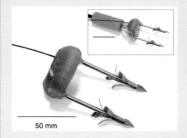

50 mm

ABOVE A satellite-linked tag with limpet attachment darts.

RIGHT Spring migratory tracks of humpback whales tagged in Hawaii between 1995 and 2000.

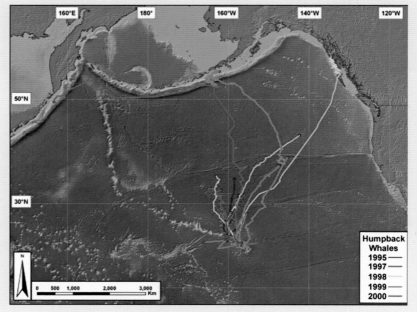

EFFECTS OF ENVIRONMENTAL VARIATION ON THE REPRODUCTIVE CYCLE

Changes in food availability may result in changes to pregnancy or birth rate, similar to those described above for the age at which sexual maturity is reached. Two examples serve to illustrate this.

An analysis of data on female fin whales taken in whaling operations around Iceland found that these whales had thicker blubber (more stored energy) when there was more zooplankton prey available per whale and also that pregnancy rates were higher in whales with thicker blubber. Assuming pregnancy resulted in birth, this shows that birth rate was higher when there was more food available for each individual whale.

Further west in the Bay of Fundy, Canada, a study of right whales found that a female's blubber thickness was positively correlated with the number of years since she had given birth, indicating that a female needs to build up sufficient stores before embarking on an energy-draining pregnancy and subsequent lactation. In addition, blubber thickness was found to be thinner in years of low abundance of the copepod *Calanus*, the main zooplankton prey of right whales in the North Atlantic. Overall, this shows that less food leads to longer inter-birth intervals and therefore a lower birth rate.

Together these two examples illustrate what we might expect – that whales reproduce more slowly when there is less food and more quickly when there is more food, although the overall variation in reproductive rate may be fairly small. In the case of the fin whales, the changes in food availability per whale were driven by the population declining as a result of whaling and then recovering when whaling ceased. This can thus be seen as a density-dependent response similar to the situation for the age at which sexual maturity is reached, as described on page 56 for Southern Hemisphere fin whales. In the case of the North Atlantic right whale, however, the population is very small (around 500 whales). There is thus a concern that if the environment is changing and the whales cannot find enough food to reproduce successfully, this may hamper recovery of a very vulnerable population (see also Chapter 8).

CHAPTER 4

The greatest free-divers

WHALES ARE TRULY REMARKABLE DIVERS. A Cuvier's beaked whale has been recorded diving to a depth of almost 3 km (2 miles) and remaining underwater for more than two hours. This particular dive was exceptional, but beaked and sperm whales regularly dive to one to two kilometre (½–1¼ mile) depths for up to an hour, and do this repeatedly. Contrast this with human free-divers, who can generally reach only tens of metres and then need some time to recover from the dive. Although all whales have to return to the surface to breathe, they do so for only relatively short amounts of time. They are probably better regarded as 'surfacers' rather than 'divers', because they spend most of their time at depth with visits to the surface, rather than the other way around.

So what's down there? In the ocean, the deeper you go down into the water column the darker it gets, as different colours of sunlight are absorbed by the water. Red is absorbed first, then yellow, green and ultimately blue. From the surface of the ocean down to the lowest depth to which light reaches is called the photic zone. This depth varies depending on how murky the water is but on average extends to about 200 m (660 ft) deep. The photic zone is where photosynthesis occurs, and approximately 90 per cent of life in the ocean lives in this layer. However, some sea creatures have adapted to live in the dark depths beyond this photic zone, and some species of whales descend to these deep depths to find and eat them.

Deeper water means greater hydrostatic pressure. For every 10 m (33 ft) you descend, the pressure increases by one atmosphere (15 pounds per square inch). So even relatively shallow diving species such as a humpback whale diving to 50 m (165 ft) would experience pressures six times greater than the pressure we experience at the water surface (atmospheric pressure). However, a sperm or a beaked whale diving to 2,000 m (6,560 ft) has to be able to withstand the extreme, crushing pressure 200 times the pressure at the water surface!

Before 50 years ago, most of what we knew about diving whales came from observations from whalers in terms of the amount of harpoon line taken out, or the time whales were submerged between blows. You might think the advent of scuba (self-contained underwater breathing apparatus) would help, but in fact most

OPPOSITE A sperm whale raises its tail flukes prior to embarking on a dive. Sperm whales often dive to at least a kilometre deep.

whale species are disturbed by exhaled bubbles. Even with rebreathing apparatus (which doesn't release bubbles), we can only observe the underwater movements of relatively stationary shallow-diving species. The presence of a diver in the water also has the potential to alter the behaviour of the species being studied. To overcome these restrictions, methods of obtaining physical and biological data using animal-attached tags, called biologging, have been developed.

Biologging tags are animal-attached devices, which log and record or relay the data they collect. The earliest records of whale dives came from a device called a 'manometer', a capillary tube with dye dusting along its inner surface, such that as the air became compressed the incoming water would stain the dye. This could only provide information on the maximum depth reached – as shown by the position of the dye on the tube. To learn more about movements of the animal over time, the equipment progressed to using a moving needle recording a trace onto a smoked glass plate. Today, researchers use solid-state digital technology, enabling pressure sensors to log their readings over time.

However, the development of increasingly sophisticated technology is little help if we cannot get the tag onto the animal we want to study. The earliest manometer tags were attached to the end of harpoons and fired into whales to record their dives before they were captured. Nowadays, tags are placed on the whale remotely, either by pole, crossbow or air rifle. Smaller species (porpoises and dolphins) can be captured either incidentally in fishing nets, or deliberately as they swim on the wave created by a moving boat or ship.

Keeping a tag attached to a whale and getting the data back again are also tricky. The tag can be attached to the whale either by suction cup, for short-term deployments (hours to days), or by dart/penetrating tag for longer deployments (months) (see page 64). The tag must then either be recovered in order to download the data (with sufficient flotation for the tag to float at the surface and transmit a radio signal so the package can be found at sea), or the data can be recovered remotely (generally using the Argos system on polar-orbiting satellites, although fewer data can generally be transmitted this way).

RIGHT A researcher attaches a suction-cup tag to a humpback whale by means of a hand-held pole. Tags can also be attached to whales using a crossbow or an air rifle.

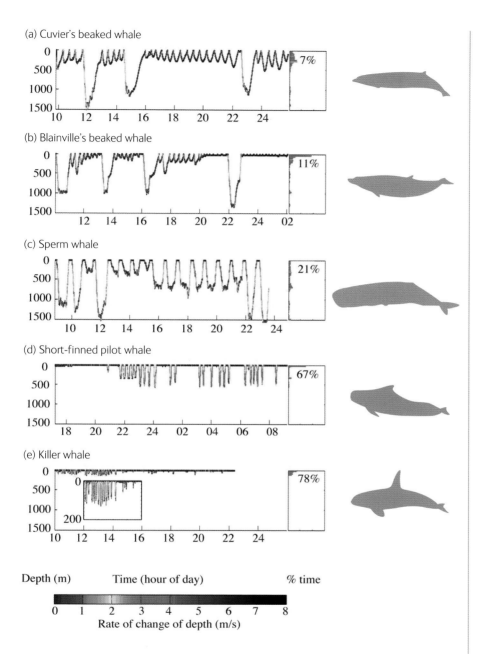

(a) Cuvier's beaked whale

(b) Blainville's beaked whale

(c) Sperm whale

(d) Short-finned pilot whale

(e) Killer whale

Depth (m)   Time (hour of day)   % time

Rate of change of depth (m/s)

LEFT Different whale species have very different diving behaviour. These plots of whale dives are drawn at the same scale, from the surface to 1,500 m (4,921 ft) depth over a period of 16 hours, and coloured according to the vertical swimming speed of the whale. The beaked and sperm whales can be seen to dive very deeply but to ascend and descend more slowly than the pilot whale and killer whale (for which an expanded inset for the upper 200 m (656 ft) is needed to see the dives more clearly). The red horizontal frequency histograms on the right of each dive trace show the distribution of the time each whale spent in 10 m (33 ft) depth intervals, with the time spent in the interval nearest the surface (0–10 m; 0–33 ft) shown as a percentage. Of these five whales, the two beaked whale species spend the least time near the surface. Datalogging tags recovered from each of these species allow us to recreate the underwater movements recorded while the tag was attached.

Using these types of biologging tags, researchers are gradually amassing a picture of the movements of animals underwater. Tags have shown how whales dive and the differences among species in the way they dive. Baleen whales tend to be near-surface feeders, diving to feed on schools of fish or swarms of krill in the photic zone. Toothed whales show a wide range of diving behaviour from river dolphins, which live in shallow river systems for their whole lives, to beaked and sperm whales, which are the deepest divers, regularly diving to depths of a kilometre (½ mile) or more. Pilot whales resemble cheetahs of the deep, with fast sprints down to depth to catch large squids. By contrast, killer whales are relatively shallow divers, occupying the upper hundred metres of the ocean.

Although these animal-attached tags can tell us what whales do underwater, we can only understand their diving physiology through insights from anatomical studies of stranded and dead whales, and from experimental work using captive and trained dolphins, which can be easier to study than whales in the wild.

All diving whales face two major problems: dealing with the higher pressure at depth, and being able to cope with long periods holding their breath. As any scuba diver will know, the major problem for diving mammals is the airspaces – and the inverse relationship between pressure and volume of gas described by Boyle's law (the volume of a gas decreases as pressure increases). As a whale dives and pressure increases, the volume of gas becomes smaller and can cause barotrauma (an injury caused by a change in pressure). We are familiar with this in terms of the ear pain felt on aeroplanes. The middle ear is essentially an air-filled rigid cavity with little or no compressibility. As the pressure increases on descent, the air space in the inner ear shrinks. This causes a difference in pressure between the air in the middle ear and the air outside the ear so that the eardrum flexes. We need to equalize this pressure by opening the Eustachian tube and allowing higher-pressure air from the throat to enter the middle ear (by sucking, swallowing or holding our nose and blowing gently).

In humans, the middle ear and the facial sinuses are problematic for diving. Diving with a head-cold can be disastrous, as a blockage can mean that rapid pressure changes cannot be equalized. Our facial sinuses lighten the skull and provide resonance for our voices, and most importantly they provide mucus that moisturizes the inner lining of the nose. Whales have lost these facial sinuses, presumably in order to avoid problems with these air-filled structures during diving. The airspace of the middle ear is necessary for hearing, but in whales this has become lined with a network of blood vessels that engorge with blood to help to fill the space as the whale dives and pressure increases. More elaborate and bigger vessels are found in the deeper-diving whales.

RIGHT Whales exhale and then inhale prior to diving. A humpback whale exhales forming a blow up to 3 m (10 ft) high off the coast of New Zealand.

However, the major airspace for diving mammals is the respiratory system. For humans, a big problem is lung squeeze, because pressure reduces the air volume within our incompressible ribcage. When humans first began to free-dive as a sport it was thought that they could not go below 30 m (98 ft) without causing the lung to shrink and the chest wall to implode. In fact, some humans can dive deeper than this, by undergoing a shift in which blood fills up blood vessels in the lungs and so offsets the shrinking air space (in the same way as the vasculature in whale ears fills to offset the reducing air volume). Whales do not need this adaptation for their lungs; they circumvent this problem by having a highly compliant chest wall and ribcage. As their lungs compress on descent, so too their ribcage folds down and air is forced from the air sacs, called alveoli, into the less compressible airways of the bronchial tubes (airways within the lungs) and trachea (see page 74).

The other major problem for whales is breath-holding – how do they get enough oxygen to maintain such long dives? Whales have several adaptations to help them achieve breath-holds that can extend for more than an hour. All mammals store oxygen in the lungs, blood and muscle. In humans, the lungs are very important stores of oxygen – we can hold our breath after inhaling longer than we can after exhaling. Marine mammals generally rely less on their lung oxygen because the lungs will collapse at depth. Oxygen travels to the rest of the body because it diffuses from the lungs into the blood, where it binds to haemoglobin, an oxygen-carrying protein found in the red blood cells. When the haemoglobin reaches oxygen-poor tissues it releases the oxygen to the tissues. A similar protein, myoglobin, is found in the muscle, where it also stores oxygen.

Cetaceans save more oxygen in the blood and the muscle than humans do. Their blood is thicker and contains more red blood cells and more haemoglobin than that of humans. They have more blood and muscle relative to their body size, and their muscles contain ten times more myoglobin than ours. This is surprising because there is normally a limit to the amount of myoglobin that muscles can contain, as too high a density of myoglobin would cause the molecules to stick together. However, whales seem to manage this by having positive electrical charges on the surface of each myoglobin molecule, which helps to repel the molecules from each other and stops them sticking together, allowing more to be packed into the small space. Muscles, and particularly the swimming muscles, of all diving animals have high concentrations of myoglobin, but this is especially true for the very deep-divers, such as the beaked whales, which have very dark, almost black, muscle tissue.

Whale lungs are particularly efficient at taking up oxygen at the water surface between dives. In a terrestrial mammal, the volume of air inhaled and exhaled in one breath, called the tidal volume, is only about 15 per cent of the total lung capacity. In whales, this is much higher – often as much as 90 per cent. In other words, they have far less 'dead space' in the lungs than other mammals. Several factors help them to do this. Their lungs contain more elastic tissue and their ribs contain more cartilage, allowing them to change shape more than those of terrestrial mammals. The ends of the airways are reinforced in marine mammals. This reinforcement allows high flow

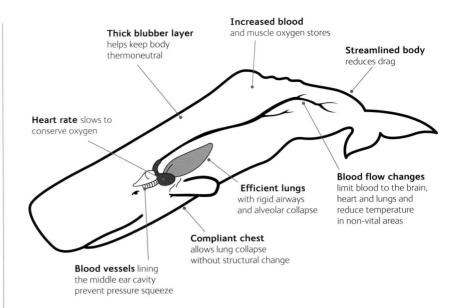

Thick blubber layer helps keep body thermoneutral

Increased blood and muscle oxygen stores

Streamlined body reduces drag

Heart rate slows to conserve oxygen

Efficient lungs with rigid airways and alveolar collapse

Blood flow changes limit blood to the brain, heart and lungs and reduce temperature in non-vital areas

Compliant chest allows lung collapse without structural change

Blood vessels lining the middle ear cavity prevent pressure squeeze

rates on exhalation even when the volume of the lungs is becoming smaller. Thus a dolphin can complete an exhalation and inhalation cycle in approximately one-third of a second. With a tidal volume of 10 litres, flow rates through the air passages can be as high as 70 litres per second.

To extend the time that an animal can spend underwater, whales use the oxygen that they have as slowly as possible. How fast an animal uses energy is known as the metabolic rate, and animals can extend the time they spend underwater by reducing their metabolic rate. All mammals have a 'dive response'. Even in humans, immersing the face in cold water will cause a reduction in heart rate. The incredible stories we occasionally hear of young children surviving 15–45 minutes under water in frigid lakes, ponds and oceans is thought to be due to this automatic reflex, which is often more robust in younger children than adults. Marine mammals have the same reflex. The heart-rate quickly becomes reduced, known as bradycardia, and there is widespread reduction in blood flow as blood is shunted from the extremities to the brain and heart. This reduction in blood flow at the peripheral arteries, called vasoconstriction, goes hand-in-hand with the reduction in heart rate to allow the blood pressure to remain constant. The reduced blood flow results in an overall reduction in metabolism, as it effectively shuts down digestion, kidney and liver function. The isolation of the muscles from circulation means that the muscles have to rely on their own oxygen stores.

Most whales are exceptionally hydrodynamic, which helps to make their movements energetically efficient. We see this in their body shape and appendages, which are modified to maximize their propulsive force (ability to push forwards) and minimize drag (force slowing the animal down). Recent work using cameras and accelerometer tags has also shown that many animals glide rather than swim whenever possible; this also saves energy. Burst-glide swimming intersperses periods of active fluking (beating the tail), with periods of gliding in which whales do not move their tail flukes, but use their buoyancy to either sink or float rather than to swim. The collapse of the lung (even for humans) means that buoyancy changes markedly with depth, and whales make the most of these buoyancy changes in their swimming motion during descent and ascent in their dives.

These various ways to help extend the dive duration may be used to differing extents by different whales. Deep-diving species rely more on blood and muscle oxygen stores, and less on the lungs for oxygen, and also tend to have smaller lungs. This is thought to be because the lungs can be a liability under higher pressure, because they are also essentially a nitrogen reservoir in addition to an oxygen store. When higher pressure causes the lungs to reduce in volume, it also causes the gas pressure to increase (the same number of nitrogen molecules are in a smaller space). This in turn increases absorption of nitrogen from the lung into the blood and body tissues. The resulting elevated levels of nitrogen in blood and body tissues can cause many of the problems that we associate with deep diving.

Human scuba divers are particularly susceptible to these problems. They breathe compressed gas at depth, and so high levels of both nitrogen and oxygen dissolve in their blood. If a diver comes up too quickly, and the nitrogen cannot diffuse back out of the blood to the lungs rapidly enough, gas bubbles emerge from the bloodstream. These can get stuck in capillaries and organs, causing pain (the condition is termed 'the bends' because pain at the joints causes divers to double up).

So why don't whales get the bends? Firstly, all marine mammals dive on a single breath of air, i.e. they free-dive. Secondly, their lung collapse is thought to further reduce the amount of nitrogen they take up. In general scuba diving is a far more dangerous pastime than free-diving because the diver inhales multiple pressurized breaths of air throughout the dive. For example, air that would be four times greater in volume at the surface is inhaled in each breath at 30 m (98 ft) depth.. Scuba divers must use dive tables to govern how long they can safely spend at depth and how much time they need to spend in decompression stops necessary to off-gas on the way back to the surface. However, free-diving can also be dangerous, and it is becoming increasingly apparent that human free-divers can also suffer from decompression sickness (DCS). In the Tuamotu Archipelago in the southern Pacific Ocean, pearl divers dive repeatedly and spend relatively little time at the surface. Occasionally such divers report

BELOW A northern bottlenose whale raises its head above the water as it spyhops. A species of beaked whale, these animals can dive to depths of 1,500 m (4,921 ft) for more than an hour.

'Taravana' diving syndrome, and suffer from vertigo, nausea, partial or complete paralysis, unconsciousness and even sudden death. This problem appears to have arisen with the use of wetsuits allowing divers to spend longer in the water.

In marine mammals, the alveoli, which are tiny sacs within the lungs that allow oxygen and carbon dioxide to move between the lungs and the bloodstream, can collapse. This also prevents diffusion of nitrogen into the blood, and so protects against decompression sickness. Physically this is assisted by their more rigid trachea and terminal airways (bronchial tubes). So, as the volume of air in the lungs (the trachea, bronchial tubes and alveoli combined) reduces under pressure during the dive, the air tends to remain in the trachea and bronchial tubes because they are more rigid, while the alveoli reduce in volume until they collapse. The deeper diving seals exhale before they dive, which helps to reduce the depth at which lung collapse occurs (because there is less air in the lungs) but cetaceans dive after inhaling. Given their need to echolocate (see page 82), this is perhaps not surprising because toothed whales require air to pass over their phonic lips to make clicks at depth (see Introduction). At 1,000 m (3,280 ft) depth, the air in the body will be only one percent of its volume at the surface, which could have severe consequences for producing streams of clicks. In fact, once their air chamber empties, whales may need to recycle the air, passing it back from air sacs in the upper respiratory tract into the chamber, before more clicks can be made.

The collapse of the alveoli raises another problem for these animals. In humans, lung collapse is a serious medical condition. Yet in whales, the alveoli are completely collapsed and then reinflated after every deep dive. In order to do this, whales have increased production of surfactants associated with the pressure of dives. The surfactant is a fluid in the alveoli that decreases stickiness or surface tension and so stops the inner surface of an alveolus from sticking to itself. This makes reinflating the collapsed alveoli upon surfacing much easier.

While lung collapse is thought to be the primary adaptation preventing increased gas concentrations in blood and so preventing whales from being subject to DCS, other adaptations potentially also provide safeguards. The retia mirabilia are a series of vascular networks of densely looped arteries primarily located from the base of the brain case and along and within the vertebral column. Various speculations as to its function include as an elastic reservoir for brain blood flow, as a system to allow the engorgement of blood vessels to reduce 'lung squeeze', or as a filter for any arterial gas bubbles.

Despite such adaptations to reduce DCS, we now have hints that cetaceans may not be completely invulnerable to it. In 2002, a series of beaked whale strandings in the Canary Islands coincided with military sonar exercises nearby (see also page 132). Intravascular bubbles were found in several organs of these whales in both stranded and floating dead animals (suggesting that it was not the stranding process that caused the bubbles to form). Similar observations have also been recorded among other single-stranded cetaceans around the UK, but at a much lower rate of incidence than during this stranding event. There have been several such beaked whale strandings coincident with military sonar exercises in the past three decades, but no further strandings in the Canaries since a moratorium on sonar was enacted there in 2004. It therefore seems likely that some change in whale behaviour renders them susceptible to bubble formation and stranding.

Old sperm whale skeletons from whaling museums have been found to show bone necrosis, similar to that found in osteonecrosis caused by repetitive diving in humans. It has been suggested that this could have been caused by the repeated formation of nitrogen bubbles in capillaries, so reducing circulation and bone health over the long term. Bubbles have also been observed in dolphins and seals fatally entangled in fishing nets at depth and brought back to the surface, suggesting that they had tissues supersaturated with nitrogen. Observations using ultrasound on live-stranded dolphins have also shown the presence of bubbles in some tissues. These animals have then survived after release, suggesting that cetaceans may be able to tolerate some degree of bubble formation without consequence. Together these observations are beginning to challenge the assumption that cetaceans are immune to DCS.

In summary, whales are highly evolved to cope with the physiological stresses of diving to depth, with their main adaptations focusing on the prevention of barotrauma surrounding their air spaces, and on lung collapse, which both prevents lung rupture and impedes gas exchange between the lungs and the rest of the body when the hydrostatic pressure is high. Increasingly, however, it seems likely that these animals are trading off their physiological dive response with other issues – buoyancy, digestion or thermoregulation. They may therefore be more susceptible to diving diseases, such as the bends, than we used to think, but in normal conditions can avoid the dangers by managing gas under pressure. However, a reaction to unanticipated events during a dive might cause animals to stretch their physiological adaptations too far and lead some individuals to run into problems.

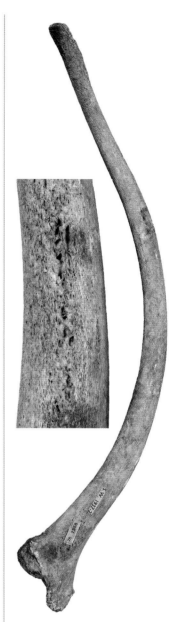

ABOVE The damage to this sperm whale's rib is a sign it has made many deep dives. The flaking happens if microscopic nitrogen bubbles form during surfacing decompression, blocking bone circulation.

CHAPTER 5

Eat and be eaten

A S WE HAVE ALREADY SEEN, the main evolutionary split within the whales separates the baleen whales from the toothed whales, and the species in each of these groups have evolved innovative feeding methods that have been an important factor in their ecological success. As their name suggests, instead of teeth, baleen whales have evolved plates of protein called baleen, which grow down from the upper jaw. Strands of baleen form a strainer, allowing baleen whales to engulf whole patches of small prey and then strain out the seawater and swallow the food left behind on the baleen. Toothed whales have to catch individual prey items but, like bats, they have evolved echolocation – producing sounds and listening for echoes of prey. Echolocation allows toothed whales to find prey at ranges of tens to hundreds of metres in murky water or in the dark, before the prey can detect the oncoming predator. While some toothed whales grab their prey, others feed by sucking their prey, and this means that whales with highly deformed jaws can lead otherwise normal lives.

OPPOSITE Broken and deformed lower jaws have often been reported for sperm whales which were otherwise healthy, perhaps because they suck rather than bite their squid prey.

BELOW A right whale opens its mouth to filter prey from the water showing the long baleen plates hanging from its upper jaws. Right whales have rough grey patches of skin called callosities on their heads. These can become encrusted with whale lice and barnacles.

BALEEN

Baleen whales include the largest animals evolved on our planet. Their large size allows them to swim efficiently over long ranges in search of prey. Many species spend their winter breeding in the tropics, and migrate to polar waters to take advantage of the pulse of productivity in higher latitudes during the summer months. Many populations have traditional foraging areas, but can easily shift hundreds of kilometres to find the largest and densest patches of their favoured prey. The ability to cover such large fractions of the ocean to find areas where they can efficiently engulf thousands of prey items at a time is the key to the global success of baleen whales.

Most baleen whales fall into two families. The balaenids (the right and bowhead whales) are bulky, slow-swimming animals that live in temperate-polar waters. They feed on small

zooplankton, especially copepods, and their baleen plates are long with fine hairs to trap the enormous quantities of small prey they need to survive. The balaenopterids, also known as rorquals, include the blue, fin and humpback whales. They migrate between low-latitude breeding areas in winter and high-latitude feeding areas in summer. These much more streamlined and faster-swimming whales feed on krill and small schooling fish, such as capelin or herring, and their baleen is consequently shorter and coarser.

The balaenids feed by opening their mouths and swimming through a dense patch of prey, with the water flowing through their baleen plates as the whale filters out the prey inside its mouth. The foraging behaviour of bowhead whales has been studied using tags (see box on page 85) that register acceleration and depth. When a bowhead whale finds a patch or layer of prey, it opens its mouth, which increases drag so much that even though it moves its tail flukes up and down continuously, it moves forward at less than one metre per second (3½ ft or 0.07 body lengths per second). This foraging mode uses oxygen and energy at a relatively high rate but allows the whale to filter a volume of 3 m³ (106 ft³) per second – up to 2,000 tonnes (2,200 tons) of water and prey per dive. The cost of this foraging requires the whales to select areas of the ocean with high prey density. Off the coast of Cape Cod, USA, right whales seldom feed where the zooplankton density is less than 1,000 animals per cubic metre.

ABOVE Antarctic krill are small in size – about 6 cm (2½ in) – but big in ecological role. They often occur in dense swarms and are the main prey for many species of whales, seals and seabirds in the Southern Ocean.

BELOW This blue whale has closed its massive mouth after a lunge and is using its baleen plates to strain food from the engulfed water.

The other group of baleen whales, the balaenopterids, feed by lunging through patches of prey and gulping large volumes of water. Their throats have an expandable pleated structure, allowing them to engulf a greater volume of water and prey than the volume of their own body. Lunging is energetically expensive for balaenopterids. To feed, they accelerate into the prey patch. As they open their mouth, the drag increases, and the energy lost through deceleration helps to open the mouth. By the time they close their mouth, they have stopped moving, so they have to reaccelerate for the next lunge. The high consumption of oxygen and energy limits the duration of their foraging dives.

Comparing a balaenopterid blue whale to a balaenid right whale of about the same body mass shows the balaenid foraging strategy to be energetically more efficient. If you divide the volume of water engulfed in a lunge by the time between lunges, most balaenopterids do not engulf more than 2 m³ (70 ft³) per second, compared with the balaenid's 3 m³ (106 ft³) per second. This allows balaenids to spend more time foraging. Over a period of 2.7 hours, a blue whale would filter only 9,000 m³ (318,000 ft³) of water and prey, half that estimated for a balaenid whale. However, between lunges, balaenopterids can move and reorient themselves to engulf a small dense patch, whereas balaenids forage most efficiently on a large patch or layer of prey. Balaenopterids can also swim 2-4 m per second to manoeuvre and chase mobile schools of prey, such as fish or krill, whereas balaenids need to target slower-swimming prey such as copepods, which are less able to evade predation.

Baleen whales obtain more benefit from filtering prey from seawater the more concentrated the prey are. Some baleen whales have evolved strategies to take advantage of the shoaling tendency of prey in response to predators, and so make them more concentrated. If prey are spread out vertically in the water column,

LEFT Humpback whales surfacing simultaneously with open mouths as they engulf a school of herring. The baleen plates can be seen hanging from the upper jaw.

humpback whales may emit bubbles, encircling the prey with a 'bubble net'. Many prey fish avoid bubbles, so they are forced to ascend and concentrate into a denser patch within the bubble net.

Gray whales also filter their food but, unusually for whales, this is mainly from the sediment rather than the water column. Gray whales dive to the ocean floor and roll onto their side using their tongue as a piston to pull large amounts of sediment with prey into their mouth. As the whales surface again, they strain the bottom-dwelling crustaceans, worms and molluscs out through the baleen, emitting a trail of mud and sand. This leaves gouges along the bottom of the sea floor.

TEETH

Toothed whales have a more standard mammalian mode of foraging than baleen whales, in which they typically search for individual prey items, approaching and capturing them one by one. Their teeth have diverged from the pattern typical of most mammals, which have different forms of teeth, such as incisors, canines, premolars and molars, to a homodont pattern in which all teeth are the same type. Toothed whales only bite and swallow their food, without chewing, so they need only canine-type teeth. Their teeth therefore do not occlude or rub against each other, so they do not become as worn as some mammalian teeth do. Unusually for mammals, in toothed whales only one (adult) set of teeth erupts from the gums, without weaker milk teeth appearing first.

Some toothed whales feed by sucking in their prey rather than grabbing them – think of sucking a piece of jelly floating in a glass of water! Over evolutionary time, the number of teeth has decreased for species (e.g. sperm whales and beaked whales), that use suction to feed on prey, such as squid, and has increased for species (e.g. dolphins, and particularly river dolphins), that seize prey, such as fish, with their teeth). Porpoise and dolphin teeth can be easily told apart – the teeth of porpoises are spade-shaped, while those of dolphins are more peg-shaped. The sperm, pygmy and dwarf sperm whales have erupted teeth only in the lower jaw, and small unerupted teeth in the upper jaw.

BELOW Dolphins, such as this common dolphin, have homodont conical teeth in both upper and lower jaws. Porpoise teeth are spade-shaped. Other toothed whales have teeth only in the lower jaw (such as sperm whales), or which have become highly modified (such as beaked whales and narwhals) and emerge only in males.

BOTTOM The teeth of the male strap-toothed whale extend above its upper jaw preventing a wide gape. These whales are thought to rely on suction for feeding.

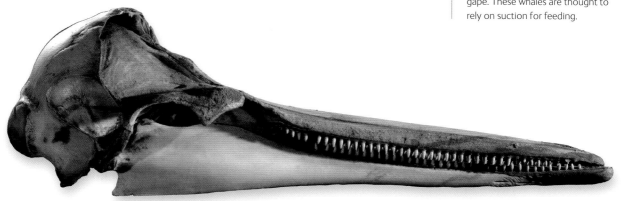

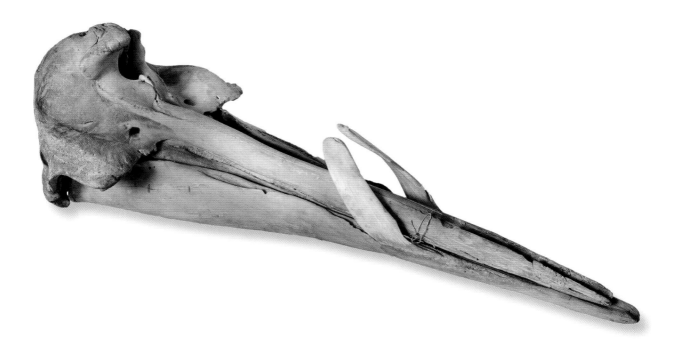

In beaked whales, teeth only erupt in the lower jaw of males, and there are large differences in the morphology (form) of these teeth among different beaked whale species. These teeth are not thought to function in prey capture at all, but rather are used for sexual selection and male–male competition. The teeth of strap-toothed whales even extend over the top of the upper jaw, preventing the mouth from opening to full capacity. This emphasizes just how non-functional for foraging teeth can become, and how these species rely on suction for capturing their squid prey. The teeth in the males of some species of beaked whales also appear to be used for male-male combat in competition with one another for females, in the same way as antlers are used in deer. These result in rake-like scars on the bodies of adult males. Sexual selection occurs when evolution by natural selection causes a genetically determined characteristic in one sex to be preferred by individuals of the other sex, or, as in this case, when the character helps members of one sex to compete for access to members of the opposite sex leading to increased reproductive success in individuals that carry the favoured characteristic.

ECHOLOCATION

Although the teeth of some species have become highly specialized, the most dramatic adaptation in the toothed whales is the way they can sense the world around them. The senses that function best in water differ from those in air. Vision is an excellent way to look at what is ahead of you in air, and many terrestrial predators are able to see prey from hundreds to thousands of metres away. But light only penetrates a few tens of metres underwater at best, limiting vision in the ocean. When mammals moved back to the sea, they had the advantage of being able to adapt the mammalian ear, which is more sophisticated than the ears of other marine organisms, such as fish. Their air-based method of click production (passing air through muscular lips beneath the blowhole) allowed toothed whales to evolve a

BELOW Clicks are produced at the phonic lips, and are focused through reflection off the skull and airsacs and passage through the melon. The echoes of these clicks are thought to be channelled through the lower jaw and are detected at the dolphin's auditory bullae.

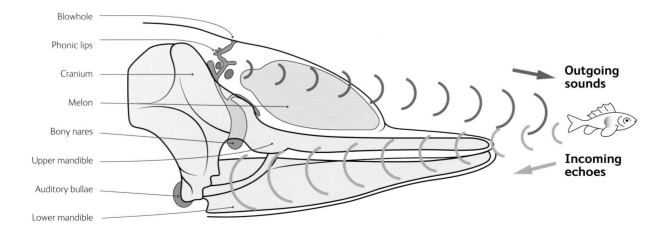

Blowhole
Phonic lips
Cranium
Melon
Bony nares
Upper mandible
Auditory bullae
Lower mandible

Outgoing sounds

Incoming echoes

powerful biological sonar, with the capacity to detect and select prey. When a whale produces a click, the sound may reflect off prey, with the whale then receiving the echo of the click when the sound is transmitted back to its ears.

Any sonar system is unable to detect rigid objects much smaller than the wavelength of the sound it emits, so low-frequency (long wavelength) sound can only be used for large objects. The speed of sound in water is about 1500 m/s, so a sound of 150,000 Hertz would have a wavelength in water of 1 cm. For a small target 1 cm (½ in) in circumference, this means that the sonar would work best operating at frequencies of 150,000 Hertz. This frequency is about 10 times higher than the upper limit of human hearing, but under selection pressures for echolocation, both bats and toothed whales have evolved hearing sensitive to frequencies this high.

The deep ocean is dark, cold and has high pressure - a challenging place for mammals that need to breathe air and maintain warm body temperatures. Yet the echolocation strategies of toothed whales have opened up a major feeding resource in the mesopelagic zone, which occurs at depths between 200 m and 1,000 m (650 ft and 3,280 ft) in the world's oceans. Mesopelagic fishes are the most abundant fish on the planet, with a biomass estimated at 10 billion tonnes (11 billion tons). These fish and mesopelagic squid form a rich foraging resource. Toothed whales have evolved at least three different ways, exemplified by sperm whales, beaked whales and dolphins and porpoises, to exploit these and coastal resources, which form the basis for their ecological success.

SPERM WHALES

Sperm whales are the largest toothed whales, with adult males growing up to 18 m (60 ft) in length and up to 57 tonnes (63 tons) in weight. Their size allows them to dive for 45 minutes or more and then recover during an approximate 10-minute surface interval. Roughly one-third of the volume of the body of a sperm whale is devoted to the spermaceti organ (see page 26), which you can think of as the largest nose on the planet. Many theories have been proffered for the function of the spermaceti organ. Some have argued that it acts as a shock absorber for a battering ram, allowing one whale to ram another one, injuring the opponent with little risk for the rammer. Another theory is that the density of spermaceti oil varies with temperature and pressure, with enough oil in the organ to allow sperm whales to maintain neutral buoyancy while diving. However, the theory most accepted today argues that this big nose makes a big noise.

According to this theory, the spermaceti organ enables sperm whales to produce a highly directional sonar click that has the highest amplitude of any sound made by an animal. Reception of the reflected clicks allows detection of a squid hundreds of metres away. This long-range sonar lets sperm whales start clicking early on a foraging dive, to find good patches of prey, and to use sonar to detect, select, approach and capture about 18 prey items per dive. Their diving capacity and long range sonar allow them to make up to 19 foraging dives per day, thus capturing more than 300 prey items a day. Changing the configuration of the sound production organ allows sperm whales to make a different kind of click, called a coda click, which is used for communication. These coda clicks do not put as much energy in a forward-directed beam, but broadcast the communication signals over a wider area, which is well suited to a dispersed audience of other whales, whose location may not always be known.

BEAKED WHALES

Beaked whales are a family of deep-diving toothed whales that are smaller than sperm whales but that can dive deeper (to nearly 3,000 m or 9,800 ft) and for longer (for more than two hours) than the deepest and longest dives of sperm whales. During these long foraging dives, beaked whales attempt to capture around 20 to 30 prey items. However, they often need more than an hour making shallow dives to rest before they take another deep foraging dive. It is thought that beaked whales dive for longer than can be supported by the oxygen they carry, so they push themselves beyond this limit (as sprinters do) and then require time to recover. Their sonar is thought to be capable of detecting squid at ranges of only 50 to 100 m (165 to 330 ft), which is much less than their typical foraging depths of more than 500 m (1,640 ft). Therefore beaked whales need to select the locations where they dive carefully to maximize their chances of encountering good foraging patches at depth. Several species of beaked whales seem to have preferred foraging areas, where rich accumulations of prey may help avoid the need to spend long periods searching for patches of food. By contrast, the long-range sonar of sperm whales allows them to scan the depth beneath them and thus range over broad areas of ocean, searching for prey below.

DOLPHINS AND PORPOISES

Dolphins and porpoises generally use sonar for finding and tracking down prey. Some species, such as the river dolphins, live in murky turbid rivers, where vision is unhelpful. Coastal porpoises and dolphins tend to echolocate more when visibility is restricted at night or in turbid water, but they echolocate most of the time, with scarcely a minute going by without them probing their environment with sound. However, the tendency for some species, such as bottlenose dolphins, to feed preferentially on fish that make sounds themselves, suggests that dolphins may also find prey by listening for prey sounds.

Oceanic dolphins also feed in the mesopelagic zone, but they do not have the capacity of sperm or beaked whales for prolonged diving. One solution to limited diving capacity is to forage at night when some mesopelagic prey move towards the surface. Species such as pantropical spotted dolphins in Hawaii do indeed appear to do this. Diving behaviour during the day is limited to the upper 50 m (165 ft) of the water column, but at night dives to 200 m (660 ft) with greater speeds are observed. Short-finned pilot whales off Tenerife also dive more regularly and have more prey capture attempts during night-time dives. However, this species has also developed a sprinting-type of dive seen during the day, when prey tend to be deeper. These daytime dives tend to only have one attempt to capture prey, which is preceded by a sprint at speeds of up to 9 m (30 ft) per second. These deep sprints contrast with how most air-breathing divers are predicted to forage, with emphasis on steady, low energy-cost swimming to maximize foraging duration. Rather these sprints seem to target high-value, highly evasive prey such as giant squid.

DIGITAL ACOUSTIC RECORDING TAGS

Sound travels far better than light underwater, and toothed whales have evolved to use echolocation to detect, select and capture their prey. Thinking about the senses that these animals use underwater, led teams of scientists and engineers to develop tags that not only record the depths and accelerations that describe the movements of these whales and dolphins, but also record the sounds they hear and make when capturing their prey. Sound needs to be recorded at higher rates than most ecological sampling, and this generates such quantities of data that available battery capacities and data storage capacities limit these tags to recording for a day or so. Because there is no need for the tag to remain on the animal for an extended period of time (unlike the tags used to track animal movements – see page 64), these tags can be attached non-invasively using suction cups. The tags are larger than biopsy darts and are often best deployed using a pole. Not only can these tags record outgoing clicks, but in some species, such as beaked whales, the tag can also record echoes from prey. This way, the tag functions like a fish-finder, using the animal's own clicks to record when the whale detects prey, when it locks on to one prey item to approach it, and when it attempts to capture prey. These acoustic recording tags have provided amazing detail of how a toothed whale uses echolocation to forage in the dark waters one kilometre (½ mile) or more below the surface.

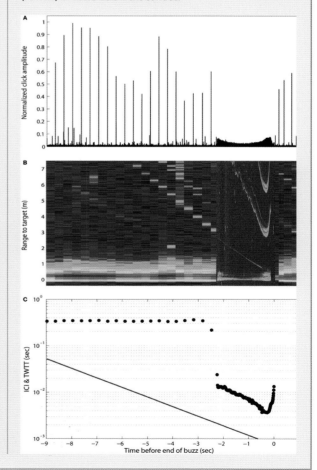

UPPER RIGHT: Amplitude of outgoing clicks recorded from a tag attached to a foraging beaked whale. A series of clicks so rapid that the individual clicks cannot be seen on the plot (called a buzz) starts a little before −2s and ends at 0s. Before the buzz, the whale makes more intense individual clicks at a rate of several per second.

MIDDLE RIGHT: Echogram display showing echoes from targets within 7 m (23 ft) of the clicking whale. The red band across the bottom shows the high energy of the outgoing clicks as recorded from the tag on the whale. The light blue rectangle appearing at −5s, at a range of about 7 m (23 ft), is a prey, the distance to which decreases as the whale approaches it. At −2s, at a distance of 3 m (10 ft), the whale switches from slow search clicks to a buzz. From here, the width of the vertical bands of colours (determined by the interval between clicks) changes resolution because the interval between clicks in a buzz is much shorter. The v-shaped lines at greater ranges in the buzz zone represent the next click in the buzz, visible because the repetition rate of buzz clicks is higher than the time required for a click to travel to a target 7 m (23 ft) away and back again.

BOTTOM RIGHT: This figure shows how the time between echolocation clicks, the inter click interval (ICI) represented by the points, changes as the whale approaches the prey. The solid line is the total time taken for a click to reach the prey and the echo to return to the whale. As the whale approaches, it maintains a steady ICI that is longer than the travel time of the click to the prey and back, and then it rapidly shortens the ICI to be closer to the return travel time during the buzz.

FINDING OUT WHAT AN ANIMAL EATS

There are various ways to study the foods that animals eat, but all have biases associated with them. If we watch an animal and record food observed at the surface, we are likely to miss any food that that an animal eats at depth. If we open up the stomach of dead animals – those washed up on the beach, or those killed accidentally (caught in fishing nets or killed by ship strikes), or even those killed deliberately – we will find remains of their food that, with practice, can be identified to the species of prey they come from. However, the hard parts that are found in the stomach – the otoliths (ear bones of fish), or the beaks of squid – are more able to withstand the stomach acids, so we are more likely to find them than we are to find a gelatinous or easily digestible prey. The same is true looking at hard parts of diet from faecal samples – only the hardest and robust parts will be identifiable after passing through the body.

An alternative is to use DNA to identify prey. Whales tend to defecate at the surface prior to diving, and observant researchers can collect a sample of the faecal matter using a fine mesh net. Some researchers use dogs trained to detect the scent of whale faeces in air, which they can locate hundreds of metres away! Using a reference database of prey samples, the DNA present in the faeces can be identified to species. While this method can accurately detect prey in the diet, it does not provide information on the relative proportions of these different prey items in the diet. Stomach and faecal samples also only provide information on the diet of the previous few days.

Two other techniques analyse the dietary components of skin and blubber from biopsy samples, small samples of skin and blubber collected using darts fired from a crossbow or air rifle. These techniques are based on the principle that the relative amounts of fatty acids and the composition of stable isotopes of chemical elements from an animal's diet will be reflected in its tissues. Some specific fatty acids are conserved through the food chain so that their signatures will reflect those of their prey species. Marine prey species tend to have distinct fatty acid signatures, which can provide detailed information about the diet of marine predators. In whales and other marine mammals, the blubber layer is the most important site of fat storage (see page 28), and analyses of fatty acid signatures in samples of blubber can be used to assess differences in diets of individuals. These analyses provide information on an animal's diet over the time period that compounds from food are stored in the blubber, typically weeks to months.

ABOVE LEFT The mouth parts of this giant squid show the two-part beak common to all cephalopods. These beaks are not digested and thousands can accumulate in a whale's stomach. Experts can identify different squid species from their beaks, measurements of which can provide an indication of squid size.

LEFT A researcher on board the R/V *Odyssey* collects a small sample of skin and blubber from a fin whale off the coast of Massachusetts, USA using a biopsy dart fired from a crossbow. A stopper prevents the dart penetrating beyond a few centimetres. The second researcher stands by as a backup in case the first misses.

Stable isotopes (different versions of a chemical element that differ in mass and do not decay) occur for many elements. For example, carbon generally has an atomic mass of 12 (six protons and six neutrons), written as ^{12}C. However, one per cent of carbon has an atomic mass of 13 (six protons and seven neutrons), forming the heavier version of carbon, ^{13}C. Different isotopes of an element are used preferentially in biochemical reactions, causing enrichment or depletion of the heavier isotope relative to the lighter one. This process of isotopic change, called fractionation, changes the ratios of stable isotopes as they pass up the food chain from one trophic level to the next when one organism eats another. Differences in fractionation also occur in different environments when phytoplankton fix carbon during photosynthesis.

Carbon $^{13}C/^{12}C$, nitrogen $^{15}N/^{14}N$ and sulphur $^{34}S/^{32}S$ are the three stable isotope ratios most commonly used for dietary analyses. Enrichment of three parts per thousand in the $^{15}N/^{14}N$ ratio at each trophic level allows inferences to be made about the position of prey on the food chain and the structure of food webs. Carbon and sulphur stable isotope ratios are generally more useful in assessing differences between ecosystems, e.g. inshore versus offshore, benthic versus pelagic, freshwater versus marine.

When an animal eats something, the food is digested, circulated around the body and then stored, and the dietary history can been seen at different timescales in different body tissues. Blood can provide information about the diet over the last few days, muscle and blubber over the previous months, and bone or teeth over a period of years. Stable isotope analyses can also be conducted on bone material from museum collections, offering the unique opportunity to investigate the historical diet of animals in a particular area and compare this to the current diet to see if a species has changed its diet over time. Similarly, there is the potential for looking at the dietary history of an individual animal over time (e.g. looking at annual growth layers of teeth (see page 52) to investigate dietary change over an individual's lifespan).

Technology-based methods of inferring diet are also available. Video cameras can show us what an animal has in its field of view when it is underwater, but it is often difficult to position the camera with a view of the mouth to observe ingestion. Accelerometers can show us the bursts of swimming speed during prey chases, although they cannot tell us whether those chases were successful. For animals such as seals, which can be captured and held while instrumentation is attached, a temperature sensor can be placed in the stomach, which can show when prey are ingested, because the stomach temperature of a warm-blooded mammal drops when a cold fish arrives in the stomach. However, restraining a whale to put a sensor in the stomach is not possible.

BELOW Stable isotope variation for whales in the North Atlantic. Isotopic nitrogen indicates the trophic level at which the whales are feeding. Isotopic carbon shows differences between inshore and offshore, or benthic and pelagic ecosystems.

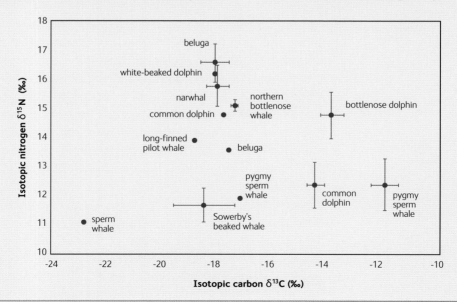

PREDATOR-PREY INTERACTIONS

All species within an ecosystem are linked in terms of their interactions; individuals of one species may eat those of another or they may compete with each other for prey or other resources, such as shelter. Predators and prey may affect each other's evolutionary history, shaping each other's behaviour, physiology, morphology and life history strategies. In particular, the sensory basis of predator–prey relationships can resemble an arms race in which predators are selected to find prey without being detected themselves, and prey are selected for detecting early warning of predator attacks. For example, the hearing of most fish species is limited to frequencies so low that they may not be able to hear the high-frequency echolocation clicks of toothed whales. However, a few herring species have specialized hearing that can detect loud, high-frequency sounds. These species react to brief high-frequency clicks like the echolocation clicks of toothed whales by swimming away to reduce the risk of predation.

Most whales and other marine mammals have ecological roles as both predators and prey within their particular ecosystem. They feed on their prey and try to avoid their predators. However, killer whales are the ultimate 'top' predator, commonly feeding on other whales as well as seals, birds and fish. Different types of killer whales seem to specialize on different types of prey.

The so-called resident killer whales living off the coasts of Washington State and British Columbia feed on salmon. They produce regular series of loud echolocation clicks when foraging, but these loud clicks do not warn the prey because the salmon cannot hear them. However, a second type of killer whale in the area, Bigg's (or transient) killer whales, feed on acoustically sensitive marine mammals (such as harbour seals or porpoises) and therefore adopt a cryptic echolocation strategy, producing fewer clicks with irregular timing. Some of the smaller toothed whales such as porpoises, *Cephalorhynchus* dolphins and pygmy/dwarf sperm whales have evolved narrow-band high frequency echolocation clicks, with most of their energy above the frequencies that killer whales can hear. This echolocation strategy is thought to have evolved in these three separate toothed whale groups to reduce the risk of being detected by killer whales. However, this acoustic hiding strategy comes at a potential cost for those species, because these higher-frequency clicks do not travel very far (a few hundred metres), thus reducing the range over which these animals can use echolocation to sound out their environment and find prey.

Deep-diving beaked whales produce clicks that killer whales can hear, but seldom in waters shallower than about 200 m (660 ft), much deeper than the depths at which killer whales usually hunt. The surface, where these whales must come to breathe, has a much higher risk of predation for them. Beaked whales tend to spend little time on the surface and are silent on ascent and descent. However, in spite of this cryptic strategy, killer whales have been observed eating beaked whales at the surface.

Many species that are prey of whales adopt a schooling strategy to reduce the risk of being detected and captured. When prey form concentrated schools, a hunting

whale is less likely to encounter them than if they are spread out more evenly. In response to this, some toothed whales coordinate their foraging behaviour to improve the chances of finding sparse schools of prey. When searching for schooling prey, these whales or dolphins may spread out in a line perpendicular to their direction of movement, separated by distances that match their echolocation range, so that they can sweep through the largest possible area, looking for prey schools. You might think that one school of fish would be hard to find in the vast expanse of ocean, but if a school of dolphins spreads out to search in a line a mile wide, their odds of detecting that school are greatly increased. In contrast, we do not have a good idea of how baleen whales find schooling prey.

Once whales detect a school of prey, their next task is to catch the prey within the school. As mentioned above, the baleen whale strategy of engulfing whole patches of prey turns the schooling behaviour of prey to the whale's advantage. When prey form a patch that is too large for one whale to engulf, groups of whales may forage side by side, simultaneously engulfing most of the patch. With highly mobile and evasive prey such as herring, groups of humpback whales may learn coordinated ways to cooperate to concentrate and capture prey. In Alaska, it has been found that one whale in the group may make a series of trumpeting sounds to synchronize and coordinate whales hunting herring.

ABOVE Bigg's (or transient) killer whales feed on marine mammals, like this harbour seal, and can sometimes be seen to toss their prey into the air, reminiscent of a cat playing with a mouse.

Compared with baleen whales, toothed whales are at a disadvantage when feeding on schooling prey, as they can only take one or a few items at a time. When killer whales feed on herring, they have a strategy called carousel feeding, in which a group encircles the herring school, with individual killer whales taking turns to take a few fish. It takes considerable coordination for the rest of the killer whales to maintain the integrity of the herring school while one enters the school to feed.

In a similar manner, a group of bottlenose dolphins in Florida has developed a novel method of herding fish, known as mud-ringing. The dolphins work as a team - one dolphin swims in a circle near to the shallow mud sea floor, and pumps its tail to beat the mud up into the water. The mud rises and panics the fish, causing them to try to escape from the ring. The dolphins line up outside the circle and simply catch the fish as they leap over the muddy water.

There are advantages for predators to hunt in groups even when they are not hunting schooling prey. When killer whales feed on mammals, their feeding success is higher when they hunt in small groups of about three whales. Like lions feeding on antelope on the plains of Africa, a coordinated group of killer whales may be more successful in capturing a seal or porpoise. For example, when a seal detects

ABOVE RIGHT In shallow water off the coast of Norway, an adult male killer whale appears through a gap in a school of herring created by a rapid downward movement of the tail flukes to stun some of the fish.

RIGHT Bottlenose dolphins off the coast of Florida, USA have learnt to form mud-rings around schools of fish that panic and jump away from the mud into the mouths of other dolphins.

hunting killer whales, it can sometimes escape to a hiding site such as a crevice in the sea floor. When killer whales are in a group, they can alternate time at the bottom, waiting for the seal to come out when it runs out of air. A lone killer whale by contrast would have to break off its bottom patrol to surface to breathe. When killer whales hunt for seals or porpoises in groups, the whale that kills the prey often shares it with group-mates. Killer whales have also been observed feeding on large baleen and sperm whales. When one prey animal can feed many, killer whales often feed in larger groups, which may also enable more efficient hunting strategies.

Many cetaceans also form schools and coordinate behaviour under the threat of predation. Predation risk is thought to be an important driver of the very large schools found among oceanic dolphin species. Oceanic dolphins have nowhere to hide, so concentrating into a school may make them harder to detect, as previously discussed for their prey.

Sharks are also significant predators of whales, particularly dolphins and whale calves. The biggest threat that a shark poses for a whale is if the shark can sneak up on the whale undetected. In this case, the shark can attack first, but if a toothed whale detects a shark from sufficient range, it may be able to outmanoeuvre and avoid the shark. The key therefore is to detect the shark before the shark can attack. Schools of animals may be more likely to detect an approaching predator and do so at a longer range. One simple way to achieve this is for animals to take turns being vigilant and

ABOVE A strap-toothed beaked whale suffers a fatal attack by a group of killer whales on the continental shelf edge 40 km (25 miles) off the south coast of Western Australia. The killer whales stripped the skin from the beaked whale, exposing the blubber, before dragging it underwater.

looking for predators. All animals have to spend some time attending to matters other than predators so, if a scout can raise the alarm for the whole group, even animals who are not paying attention to predators can be protected by the lookout.

Using the whole school to increase vigilance is particularly important for animals that rely on directional sensory systems. Vision and echolocation are directional, so an animal can only detect predators that are in its field of view. The more animals looking for predators within a group, the better the coverage of all directions the threat could come from. Highly social animals with well-developed communication systems, such as the toothed whales, are not only better adapted to finding prey when they hunt in groups, they are also better adapted to detecting predators when the whole group can integrate the sensory information being gathered by every member of the group.

Some toothed whales also have social defences against predators or competitors. For example, when tuna fish migrate through the Straits of Gibraltar, pilot whales and killer whales in the area feed on this rich food source. Even though killer whales are deadly predators of marine mammals, large groups of pilot whales may mob a smaller group of killer whales and drive them out of the area. Beaked whales go silent when they hear killer whales and other species that echolocate at high frequencies and use cryptic behaviour to avoid detection by killer whales. But whales that rely on social defences may call to increase their social cohesion when they detect killer whales in the area.

Sperm whales have a well-defined social defence against predators. In the face of predation threat, a sperm whale group will form a 'marguerite' formation (named after the daisy), in which adults form a circle around calves or injured adults, with their heads innermost and tails ready to strike at any attacking predator. This defence is often successful against killer whales, but less so against human whalers, who used this defence to their advantage. Whalers would often harpoon one sperm whale in a group, and then leave it in the water while they killed every other member of the group, which stayed near the wounded whale to protect it. Ironically, the reason this behaviour has been so well defined is that it was observed so many times from whaling vessels.

RIGHT Sperm whales form a 'marguerite' group defence against attack from predatory whales (e.g. killer or pilot whales) or human hunters, in which adults surround young, weak or injured group members with their powerful flukes facing outwards.

THE ECOLOGICAL ROLE OF WHALES IN THE MARINE ENVIRONMENT

Whales occupy a variety of niches, ranging from feeding on some of the smallest zooplankton, to chasing and killing the largest organisms in the ocean. The ecosystem relationships between whale predators and prey occur over large spatial and temporal scales, with changes in the abundance of either affecting the other. This makes it difficult to generalize about the consequences of any ecosystem change. However, it is generally accepted that whales fulfil important functions that help to maintain and support stable and healthy ecosystems. Whales are everywhere and abundant as a group and may exert influence on, and enhance the stability of, the marine ecosystems that support them by shaping the behaviour of their prey and thus influencing the flow of nutrients through the food web. This process, known as a trophic cascade, is well established for terrestrial ecosystems (e.g. think of wolves keeping deer populations under control which in turn reduces grazing pressure on young trees and allows a whole forest to grow) and is likely to be equally important in the marine environment.

One example illustrates the potential for whale predation to cause ecosystem shifts. Killer whale predation on sea otter populations in southwest Alaska can switch an ecosystem from a kelp forest (in which otters predate urchins and so reduce grazing on kelp), to an urchin barren (in which killer whales predate the otters, allowing plentiful urchins and high grazing density).

It has been suggested that the killer whale predation on sea otters in southwest Alaska may even have been triggered by these whales 'feeding down the food web' as their large whale prey were

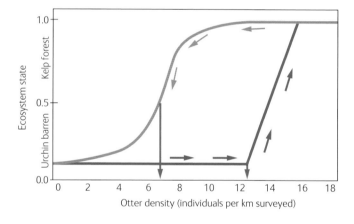

ABOVE AND LEFT Otter density is critical to ecosystem state. The graph shows that low otter density results in high numbers of urchins and a resulting urchin barren (picture far left). High otter density results in a shift in the ecosystem state in which otter predation on urchins allows the kelp forest to thrive (picture near left).

removed during the industrial whaling era and they switched diet sequentially to seals and then otters. Such top down control emphasizes the importance that marine mammals can have in structuring the marine ecosystem. Whales remove about the same biomass as human fisheries from many ecosystems, and both of these top-down drivers may affect ecosystems in complex ways. However, it can also be argued that changes in physical properties of the ocean and in biological processes lower in the food chain are equally important for regulating marine ecosystems from the bottom up. Whether the mechanism is top-down or bottom-up, resulting ecosystem shifts are difficult to predict and are not always recoverable.

Whales and other marine mammals are sometimes considered useful indicators of ecosystem health. How many there are, and where they are found is related to populations of other animals lower down the food chain. This means that changes in marine mammal distribution, abundance and behaviour may indicate changes in other parts of the ecosystem. As a practical example of how this idea can be used, the Oslo-Paris (OSPAR) Convention, established to protect and conserve the North-East Atlantic and its resources, has developed Ecological Quality Objectives (EcoQOs) for selected features of the environment. Each EcoQO defines a target based on a reference level for a specific measure of quality - for example, no more than a 10% decline over a period of 5 years in regular and systematic counts of animals of a particular species. The idea is that EcoQOs can be assumed to represent the state of the environment; a large decline in the numbers of a species could be indicative of poor ecosystem health.

However, while this may be applicable to less mobile species, many marine mammal species are highly mobile and can forage over entire ocean basins. Their ability to move across so many ecosystems means that they may not be optimal indicators for local problems, as they can integrate effects over large areas. The foraging strategies of many species seem adapted to allow them to weather bad conditions in many places and times as long as they can find good foraging at other times and places. These adaptations may therefore make wide-ranging marine mammals more resilient to ecosystem changes and less sensitive indicators of such ecosystem changes.

Whales may also play a role as marine ecosystem engineers. The feeding and diving behaviour of deep-diving whales creates the so-called 'whale pump', whereby whales transfer nutrients from the depths, where they feed, to the surface, where they defecate. Whale faeces contain important nutrients that in turn are required by phytoplankton, the key organisms at the base of all important marine food webs. Iron is a limiting nutrient in the Southern Ocean because it is crucial to phytoplankton but occurs in very low concentrations in the surface waters where phytoplankton grow. Recent studies have calculated that the iron content in whale faecal plumes is more than ten million times that of Antarctic seawater. By defecating in surface waters, blue and fin whales fertilize their own feeding grounds with nutrients needed to sustain phytoplankton, which in turn sustain the growth of the whales' krill prey. To use a terrestrial analogue again: think of cows fertilizing the meadow where they will

OPPOSITE TOP Sperm whales off Sri Lanka return to the surface where they defecate after feeding at depth, adding valuable nutrients to the relatively nutrient-poor tropical surface waters.

OPPOSITE BOTTOM Whales often defecate as they lift their tail flukes into the air before diving. Red excrement is indicative of the krill diet of this blue whale off the Channel Islands in California, USA.

later be grazing. Thus, whale populations recovering from industrial-scale whaling in the twentieth century might actually help to increase, or at the very least help to sustain, krill biomass in polar waters.

Some go as far as to say that whales could contribute to a benign form of geoengineering. Whale faeces stimulate phytoplankton growth. When phytoplankton die and are not consumed they slowly sink into the abyss, taking with them the carbon they absorbed during photosynthesis. Thus, dead phytoplankton could act as a carbon sink, removing carbon dioxide from the atmosphere and surface waters and sequestering it into the deep ocean. More whales producing more faeces, which helps to produce more phytoplankton, could therefore assist in reducing global carbon and help to mitigate the effects of climate change.

Even in death whales can influence both terrestrial and marine communities. A dead whale washing ashore will provide a welcome opportunity for terrestrial scavengers ranging from bears to beetles. A study using remote cameras around a dead humpback whale in Glacier Bay, Alaska, chronicled a four-month long 'blubber bonanza' as multiple wolves and brown bears scavenged, at times simultaneously, on the carcass. This single whale provided a substantial food resource for these terrestrial scavengers, altering their usual movement patterns and how the different species interacted. When a whale dies at sea, its carcass usually sinks to the bottom of the ocean, where it provides food and habitat for many species that only exist on these 'whale falls'. A whale carcass becomes an oasis, providing energy to

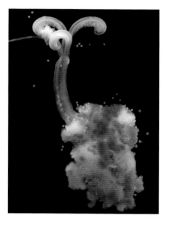

LEFT This gray whale carcass was deliberately sunk to the seafloor at 1,674 m (5,492 ft) depth as part of an experiment. After six years, the whale fall community included bacteria mats, clams in the sediments, worms and other invertebrates.

ABOVE Zombie worms – named for their bone-eating habits – extract nutrients from whale bones by boring holes into them and dissolving the bones with acid secretions.

scavengers in successional stages similar to regeneration of wasteland. At first, dense aggregations of mobile scavengers – hagfish, crabs, sleeper sharks and amphipods – strip soft tissue from the carcass. This is followed by dense aggregations of polychaete worms. The worms then disappear and the whale enters the sulfophilic phase – supporting organisms that thrive on the sulphide produced by decay of the bones – dense bacterial mats, mussels, clams and tube worms. Other bone eaters such as zombie worms might also dig deep into the bones. Zombie worms secrete an acid that dissolves the bone and use bacteria in their bodies to digest the fat and protein released from the whale bone. Zombie worms were only discovered in 2002, but they seem to have had an appetite for whale bones for millions of years because their characteristic boreholes have been found in fossil bones. So, in addition to their better-known roles as predators and prey in the water column, when they fall to the sea floor dead whales can provide the ecosystem needed by these diverse deep-sea organisms.

CHAPTER 6

Whale culture

A BEHAVIOURAL FIELD SCIENTIST HAS JUST announced the discovery of a traditional culture in which adult males spend their summers in polar regions working throughout long 16+ hours of sunlight each day, building up resources so they do not have to work for the other half of the year. This double-time work schedule allows them to spend each winter in the tropics, devoting their time to learning musical traditions shared among every adult male in their community. One large community produces songs of such high value that year after year their new improvizations are taken up by neighbouring communities, slowly spreading thousands of miles from community to community. This process may take long enough that the musical style of the outlying communities lags years behind the cultural centre, which continues to innovate its parade of hit songs.

It is reasonable to interpret the previous paragraph as describing a human culture, because terms such as 'culture' and 'music' usually apply to humans. Anthropologists traditionally limited use of the term 'culture' to humans, but there has been growing interest in studying the cultures of different animal groups, starting with our primate relatives. The case described above involves humpback whales, which feed during the summer in Antarctic waters, migrate to tropical islands during the autumn, and sing during the winter breeding season. This chapter explores how the concept of culture broadened from humans to animals, and discusses the critical elements of animal cultures.

An animal can learn to solve a new problem all by itself, called individual learning, or it can learn to solve the problem by observing or interacting with another animal that knows how to do so, in a process called social learning. A key element of culture is that cultural traditions are passed down from one generation to another through social learning. We now know that it is not just humans who learn important skills from one another and pass learned traditions from one generation to another – some other animals do so as well.

Early studies looked at primates that learnt different ways of foraging from others in their group. During the 1950s, at a time when most Western researchers focused on simple learning in individual animals, Japanese primatologists learnt to identify every individual in groups of Japanese macaques. They noticed

OPPOSITE Humpback whales are known for bubble feeding behaviour, in which they swim in decreasing circles while creating bubble clouds or curtains around a school of fish. The whales then lunge upwards to engulf the fish concentrated at the surface.

ABOVE A humpback whale displays lobtail feeding behaviour in Cape Cod Bay, USA. The whale lifts its flukes out of the water and brings them down onto the surface of the water hard and fast, making a loud slap.

that a 1.5-year-old female developed a new behaviour that had not been seen before - washing the sand off sweet potatoes by putting them in water. This new behaviour spread to other monkeys over several years, typically from a young monkey to its playmates (called horizontal transmission) or to older ones within its kinship group, until it became relatively well established. After this point, the behaviour typically spread from mothers to their infants, from one generation to the next (called vertical transmission). This study was remarkable in being among the first to use the word 'culture' for animals and in documenting so carefully the transmission patterns of social learning – how a new behaviour spreads from the initiator through the group.

More recently, mathematical models have been developed to test different hypotheses about how a new characteristic spreads through a population. For example, a genetic model would predict that the characteristic comes from the parents. One model for learning is based upon the assumption that animals are more likely to learn a characteristic from animals with which they closely associate. The idea here is that you are more likely to learn from animals you observe frequently. The way to test which model is most likely to be correct is to compare the predictions of several models to actual observations of how a learnt characteristic spreads through a population. An early application of this analysis concerned a new feeding behaviour in humpback whales, called lobtail feeding. Humpback whales feed every summer in

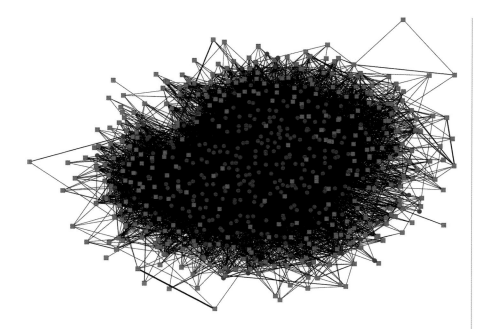

Social network of humpback whales in Cape Cod Bay, Massachusetts, USA. The blue dots indicate whales sighted lobtail feeding, and the red dots indicate whales sighted at least 20 times but never lobtail feeding. The closer the dots, the stronger the association between the whales.

Cape Cod Bay, where researchers on whale-watching boats observe foraging whales most days. Humpback whales in Cape Cod Bay often release bubbles below a school of fish, apparently to concentrate prey near the surface, before they lunge through the bubbles to feed at the surface (see pages 79 and 98).

In 1980, there was a single observation of a new twist to bubble feeding, in which the whale lobtailed, or slapped the surface, one to four times before starting to bubble feed. No one knows exactly why whales do this, but it is thought that it might concentrate a particular kind of prey called sandeels (sandlance in North America). An analysis of more than 70,000 sightings of more than 650 whales which were observed 20 or more times showed that this new form of lobtail feeding spread through the whale population over 27 years. Having a mother who used lobtail feeding did not predict whether the calf would learn this behaviour. Most learning occurred after weaning, after the calf had separated from the mother. There was thus little support for genetic factors nor for vertical transmission of lobtail feeding. The observed sequence by which whales showed lobtail feeding strongly supported social learning via horizontal transmission. The association patterns of humpback whales in Cape Cod Bay (above) show that the lobtail feeders (blue dots) tend to associate with one another more than they do with the non-lobtail feeders (red dots).

Another important form of animal culture involves vocal traditions that are learnt. Over a century ago, Charles Darwin drew parallels between the songs of birds and human music, including the observation that many songbirds learn to sing by listening to the songs of others. Electronic recorders had not been developed at this time, but researchers transcribed birdsong using musical notation. Since the time of Darwin, electronic recording has revolutionized our ability to study the vocal sounds made by animals, making vocalizations one of the easiest of behaviours to quantify.

This capability of learning to modify the sounds you produce based upon what you hear is called vocal learning, and it forms the basis of human language and music. Vocal learning is also so well developed among songbirds that they have become the dominant animal model for studying vocal learning. When sound enters the ear of a songbird, it triggers neural signals in the auditory nerve that connect to specific parts of the brain that analyse sound. These areas connect to the parts of the brain that control the muscles that produce song, a feedback that is required for vocal learning. These neural circuits are better mapped in songbirds than in humans. Well-controlled laboratory studies have defined when and what a young bird needs to hear to develop the normal song of its population. And studies of wild birds show that local populations that hear one another can form a vocal dialect with well-defined geographical boundaries, forming a local vocal culture.

In striking contrast to these data from songbirds, there is little evidence for vocal learning among most non-human mammals. The vocal patterns of most mammals, such as the bark of a dog or the meow of a cat, are generated by inherited circuits in the parts of the brain that control the patterns of action of muscles, and they can develop normally even in animals that never hear the typical calls of their species. Our experience with animals that we keep as pets emphasizes this difference: we are used to parrots or mynah birds being able to imitate human speech, but think how surprised you would be if your dog or cat whistled back a tune that you were singing.

The mammals for which we have evidence of vocal learning are humans, bats, elephants, seals, dolphins and whales. The keepers of a beluga whale in the Vancouver Aquarium believed that he could say his name 'Lagosi'. Another beluga whale trained by the US Navy heard divers speak through special equipment that allowed submerged divers speak to people at the surface. When this whale made speech-like sounds, one Navy diver was convinced that a human had ordered him to get out of the water.

Dolphins kept in aquaria and laboratories have been trained to imitate novel movements that they see performed by either a human or dolphin. In less controlled settings, it also appears that young dolphins may spontaneously imitate play behaviours. For example, dolphins in captivity learn how to blow bubble rings from other dolphins in their pool. Dolphins use at least three different ways to blow bubble rings, and they play with them in different ways. Some dolphins like to enlarge the ring and swim through it; others may blow two rings and fuse them together. Given this diversity of ways that dolphins make and play with bubble rings, if a naïve dolphin matches the play behaviour of an expert, this has been interpreted as providing some evidence for imitation.

Creative alterations of behaviour can also suggest imitation. For example, a scientist who observed dolphins in an aquarium in South Africa reported that after one young dolphin in an aquarium watched a guest smoking a cigarette on the other side of an underwater window, it swam over to its mother, suckled, swam back to the window and released a smoke-like cloud of milk.

Stronger evidence for imitation in dolphins comes from their ability to imitate sounds. Most mammals make sounds with their larynx, and they can only make one sound at a time. This would be a problem for toothed whales, which may need to communicate while they are echolocating. They have evolved a special sound-producing organ further up in the respiratory tract that has two independent sound sources, one in each nasal air passage. In dolphins, one of these sound sources is specialized for producing echolocation clicks, and the other is specialized for producing tones, called whistles, that change in frequency. To study vocal mimicry, scientists created new sounds like the whistles naturally produced by dolphins. The graph on page 104 shows how well a dolphin can imitate these synthetic whistles. Three pairs of synthetic sound and dolphin imitation are shown, with the arrow marking the end of the computer-generated sound followed by the dolphin's

LEFT A bottlenose dolphin in an aquarium blows a circular air bubble as a form of play.

attempt to imitate. Each individual bottlenose dolphin produces an individually distinctive whistle pattern, called a signature whistle, and dolphins that share strong social bonds learn to imitate one another's signature whistles.

Large whales are too big to be kept in captivity, so it has not been possible to study imitation in the same way as with dolphins or seals. However, the natural behaviour of some whales provides strong evidence for vocal learning. For example, biologists can study the songs of humpback whales using an underwater microphone, called a hydrophone, to record sound underwater. When they go to record humpback whales during the breeding season, they can usually hear song as soon as they put the hydrophone in the water. Unless they have special equipment though, they cannot tell in which direction the song is coming from. They have to look for the blows of whales, and go over to hear if that whale is singing. Once they find a singing whale, it is often so loud, they can hear it coming through the hull of the boat. At this point they can record song with a good signal for acoustic analysis.

As mentioned at the start of this chapter, humpback whales change their songs over time. The pattern by which most male whales within a population produce very similar songs, coupled with this pattern of change within and across years could not be generated by a process other than all of the whales tracking changes in the song and learning to produce them through vocal learning.

Over time not only do themes change, but they disappear from the song, and are replaced by new themes. Most biologists study humpback whale song in one limited geographic area, but a researcher working in Australia had the foresight to work

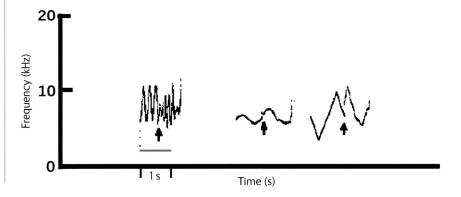

RIGHT Three examples of a synthetic whistle (left of the upward pointing arrows) followed by a dolphin mimicking that whistle (right of the upward pointing arrows). This figure is a spectrographic display which plots frequency on the vertical axis against time on the horizontal axis, similar to musical notation.

HOW DO WE VISUALIZE SOUNDS?

When a mammal hears a sound, the fluctuations in pressure in the medium (air or water) travel into the ear to the inner ear, where sound energy is converted into neural signals that the animal senses. The inner ear has a membrane that is tuned to different sound frequencies, and the more energy at each frequency hitting the ear at one time, the stronger the neural signal for that frequency. This is why when humans want to write down music, they note energy at different frequencies at different times.

When biologists want to register the sounds of mammals in a form that matches the way they and the animals hear them, they also plot frequency against time in the same way. The spectrogram plots a sound as time on the x-axis and frequency on the y-axis, paralleling musical notation.

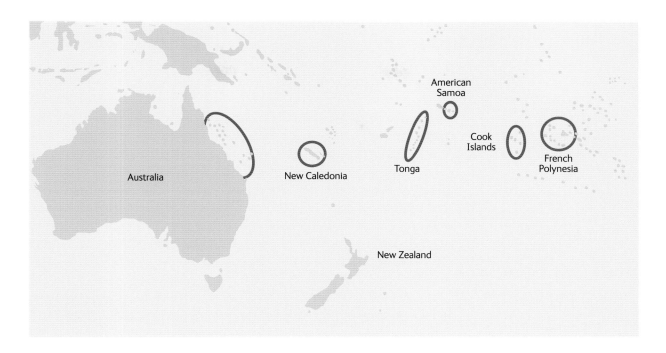

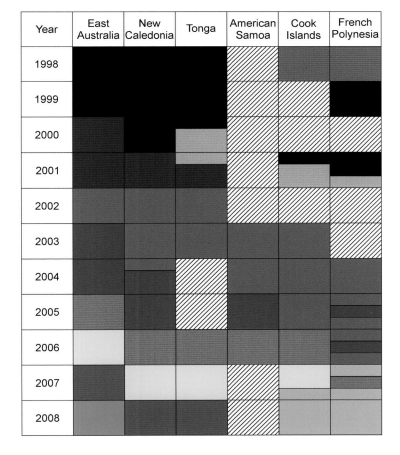

Year	East Australia	New Caledonia	Tonga	American Samoa	Cook Islands	French Polynesia
1998						
1999						
2000						
2001						
2002						
2003						
2004						
2005						
2006						
2007						
2008						

ABOVE Map of the South Pacific showing the six humpback whale breeding areas from which song was recorded.

LEFT Song types recorded from six humpback whale populations in the South Pacific over a period of 11 years from 1998 to 2008. Each song type is represented by a colour; for example, the song type coloured mid-blue started in eastern Australia in 2002 and had spread to French Polynesia by 2004.

with all the other biologists who recorded humpback songs in the South Pacific. By collaborating and pooling their data they were able to compare songs across the South Pacific from Eastern Australia to French Polynesia.

Humpback whales in the South Pacific feed during the Southern Hemisphere summer in Antarctic waters. At the end of their feeding season, each whale migrates north to the breeding ground where it was born. These breeding grounds, where females give birth to their young and where males sing, are circled in the image above. Comparing the songs from each of these breeding grounds shows that each new song type was first heard in the western South Pacific, and then spread slowly to the east. Looking at the image on the bottom of page 105, for example, you can see that the theme indicated by the light blue colour was first recorded in East Australia, New Caledonia and Tonga in 2002. By 2003 it had spread to American Samoa and the Cook Islands, and by 2004 it made it all the way to French Polynesia, at which time it was no longer heard at all in East Australia, but had been replaced by a new song type indicated by a red colour.

This one-directional pattern of horizontal transmission of song suggests that Australia acts as something like a cultural centre where new songs are generated. These songs then slowly spread thousands of kilometres to the east across the South Pacific. This pattern is reminiscent of musical styles in humans, where a hit parade is generated in cultural centres and then spreads outwards to the provinces. Today electronic transmission is nearly instantaneous, but when music was published in books and then distributed, or spread through oral traditions, the pattern might have had timing similar to that seen in the whales.

One of the fascinating things about how the songs of humpback whales change is the tension between selection for innovation (change) and selection for conformity (staying the same). There were a few years in which whales in one of these populations sang more than one song type, but the overwhelming majority of years saw all of the whales in one population singing the same song, even when song changed so much from year to year. Since there seems to be such a pressure for conformity, what is it about a new song that leads the whales to switch from their old song to the new? Of course, one might ask the same question of human popular music as well.

In spite of our bias to limit words such as 'culture' and 'tradition' to humans, Charles Darwin had a comparative evolutionary point of view that made him comfortable with arguing that animals make decisions about displays such as song that seem to be selected for aesthetic value. This was an important part of his understanding of sexual selection, in which females may select a male based upon the quality of his display. We do not yet understand how to approach the evolution of animal aesthetics, or how to understand the value of one song compared to another, but there are some cases where we can analyse the interaction between cultural evolution and biological evolution.

One of the benefits ascribed to cultural evolution is that if you have many individuals innovating and the whole population ready to take up successful solutions to problems through social learning, then cultures can adapt to changing circumstances more rapidly than the pace at which biological evolution operates. But cultural innovations can also affect biological evolution if cultural transmission is stable and strong. For example, humans are born with the ability to digest milk at birth, but in most populations the enzyme that breaks down lactose, an important sugar in milk, decreases around the time of weaning. When northern Europeans started dairy farming about 6,000 years ago, this cultural innovation created a selection pressure to retain the ability to digest milk into adulthood. Fewer than 20 per cent of adults in cultures without dairy traditions can digest milk, but selection appears to have driven this percentage to more than 90 per cent in some dairy cultures. Once the dairy tradition was established in these cultures, the use of milk as an important source of nutrition for adults has remained a stable feature of their societies for hundreds of generations, a feature that drives biological evolution.

Killer whales also have different populations with distinct foraging specializations that have been stable for enough generations to become differentiated genetically. Some of these populations have overlapping ranges and thus coexist in the same places. As previously discussed on page 88, North Pacific resident killer whales specialize in feeding on fish, especially Chinook salmon, while Bigg's (or transient) killer whales living in the same area feed on marine mammals. Killer whales live in some of the most stable social groups recorded among mammals. Neither males nor females leave their birth group, but they remain with their mothers in groups described as matrilineal groups. Closely related matrilineal groups that associate with each other most of the time are called pods. If such a pod grows too large, it may split into subgroups, each of which will form a new pod.

These pods have been studied for decades in the Northeastern Pacific. Each killer whale pod in these waters produces a group-distinctive repertoire of complex calls. It is thought that these group-specific call repertoires are used to maintain cohesion of the pod, but they may also mediate interactions between pods. These calls change slowly over time, much more slowly than the songs of humpback whales, but rapidly enough that after two matrilineally related pods split up, their versions of the same call will slowly diverge. This process of differentiation of each call type across pods, and of the overall repertoire of calls produced by each pod, creates a pattern of vocal dialects that accumulate changes over time - a form of cumulative cultural evolution that is important for human culture but has only been demonstrated for a few non-human species.

The process by which young animals develop their calls and other behaviours has not been studied in detail in killer whales. However, the pattern by which killer whales within a pod track slow changes in their calls over time suggests that young animals develop their call repertoire by experiencing calls of their pod, and that adults continue to be able to modify their calls to match acoustic models. Similarly, it is thought that young animals learn distinct foraging preferences by experiencing the behaviour of the other animals in their pod. Some killer whales beach themselves to catch seals (see page 36), and it has even been suggested that adults may teach the young how to perform this potentially dangerous foraging technique. These

RIGHT Example of different versions of the same call type recorded from four different matrilines of killer whales from Kamchatka, Russia.

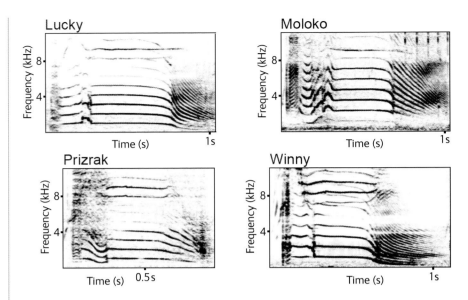

RIGHT Example of different versions of the same call type recorded from four different matrilines of killer whales from Kamchatka, Russia.

call dialects and learning of specific foraging behaviours of killer whale pods can be thought of as cultural traditions. The differences in killer whales that forage on fish versus those that hunt marine mammals are paralleled by differences in genes that affect dietary pathways. This suggests that if these traditions are stable enough over time, they may create selection pressures for biological evolution that may affect the divergence of these populations as in the case of dairy farming and enzymes for lactose.

As mentioned on page 83, sperm whales have evolved a sound production apparatus that is specialized to produce clicks for echolocation. Sperm whales do not produce non-click sounds such as those of the other whales described so far, but they do produce rhythmic patterns of click sounds, called codas, for communication. The basic unit of sperm whale societies involves a group of about 10 to 12 whales, made up of adult females, most of whom are matrilineally related, and their offspring. Sperm whales are often sighted in groups of more than one of these units. There are five distinct vocal clans in the South Pacific Ocean, based upon coda repertoires, and units preferentially join with other units from the same vocal clan. These vocal clans have overlapping ranges that extend over thousands of kilometres. Two different clans studied in the South Pacific had different movement and foraging patterns, with each of the two clans having best foraging success in different years and oceanographic conditions. These results suggest that cultural differences allow multiple social groupings of sperm and killer whales, each with specific ecological and foraging adaptations, to coexist using the same habitat in different ways.

Sperm whales are the largest of the toothed whales, with some males reaching 18 m (60 ft) in length and weighing up to 57 tonnes (63 tons). They have the largest brain of any animal, with brain weights of up to 9.2 kg (20 lbs). Killer whales are not far behind with brain weights greater than 5 kg (11 lbs) for body weights of up to 7 tonnes (7¾ tons). In addition to this large investment in brain tissue, whales have

an unusual pattern of development in which the young can swim around and sense their world at birth, but have a prolonged period of dependency. Sperm whales are born in the water after a 14- to 16-month gestation with no refuge or place to lie passively. So, on the one hand, they must be precocious at birth to swim and sense their surroundings, to breathe and to keep up with their mother. But on the other hand, large toothed whales take a long time to mature and have an unusually long period before they become independent. They not only stay with their mother for many years, but animals as old as 13 years old have been reported still to be suckling. They take solid food in the first few years of life, so this prolonged suckling may reflect a ritualization of the mother-calf bond, which has actually been prolonged for other reasons, such as learning.

It has been argued that culture may put a premium on cognitive abilities leading to selection for large brains, and that animals that must learn the culture of their group may require this prolonged period of dependency to fully master their traditions. We are still learning about the evolutionary connections between intelligence, slow maturation and culture in humans and other animals. The more species in which we can study these patterns, the better our understanding will be.

ABOVE Matrilineal groups of female sperm whales and calves produce rhythmic clicks known as codas for communication. Different groups of whales share their repertoire of codas, and so can be categorized into different vocal clans.

CHAPTER 7

Changing attitudes

HUMANS HAVE A LONG RELATIONSHIP WITH WHALES. Teeth and bones found in Stone Age middens (waste dumps) in Africa, Europe and America show that humans have been making use of whales for food, tools and ornaments for many thousands of years. Places in Europe where whale remains have been found in such middens include Skara Brae in Orkney and the Bay of Aarhus in Denmark. The whales may have been stranded or possibly caught in nets, or even driven onto the shore by small boats. The earliest evidence of active whale hunting is from the petroglyphs (prehistoric rock carvings) at Bangudae in Korea, which include several engravings of whales being hunted, dating to around five thousand years ago. Active whaling is also known to have been taking place at least three to four thousand years ago in Alaska. In the ninth century, whales were driven ashore in the English Channel for food and other commodities. Such subsistence hunting continues today, mainly in the high Arctic by indigenous peoples of Alaska, Canada, Greenland and Russia.

THE ERA OF EXPLOITATION

Commercial whaling for profit is believed to have begun in the eleventh century in the Bay of Biscay, when Basque whalers started taking right whales to provide oil for lamps in a growing European market. Right whales are so called because they had thick blubber, were slow-swimming, and floated when killed and were thus the 'right' whales to hunt. Whales were harpooned from small open boats at sea, towed back to shore, and flensed (stripped of blubber) and 'tried out' (rendered) in large iron pots to extract the oil.

Whaling escalated from the middle of the sixteenth century when the rich cod fishing grounds off Newfoundland were discovered also to be a plentiful source of right and bowhead whales. This early commercial whaling spread northeast to Svalbard and beyond to support a thriving whaling industry in the seventeenth century in the north-eastern Atlantic. The primary product was oil, but whalebone (baleen plates) was also used for various purposes, such as watch springs and stays for ladies' corsets. At this time, whales were still being captured using hand-thrown harpoons from small boats but they were now flensed alongside sailing ships and tried out on board.

OPPOSITE A boy is dwarfed by the skull of a butchered blue whale at Vågane whaling station in Norway, ca. 1918-1920. The whaling station produced cooking fat and oil, and also bone meal. Three boats captured about 180 whales per year from 1917 to 1920.

High catches year-on-year rapidly reduced local populations, and whaling fleets moved west into the Davis Strait around 1700, where they continued taking right and bowhead whales in Greenland and Canadian waters until the early twentieth century. Meanwhile, New England settlers, who had begun hunting right whales around 1650, began to take sperm whales in the early 1700s. Sperm whales have less blubber than right and bowhead whales, but the spermaceti oil in their head is very high quality and was more valuable than oil from blubber for use for lighting and as a lubricant in industrial machinery. Their large teeth were also popular for scrimshaw (decorative carving). Sperm whaling spread steadily southwards in the Atlantic and crossed the equator in 1760, following which new populations of Southern right whales were discovered off Argentina and South Africa.

In 1790, the whaling fleets rounded Cape Horn and commercial whaling was focussed in the Pacific Ocean for the next 70 years whilst also continuing in the Atlantic and Indian Oceans. Around 200,000 sperm whales were taken in tropical and temperate waters during the nineteenth century. North Pacific right and bowhead whales, Southern right whales off New Zealand and Australia, and gray whales off Baja California, Mexico were discovered during this period and hunted to commercial extinction (no longer sufficiently numerous to be worth hunting) within a few decades.

Early whaling was driven entirely by the market. There was no intention to harvest sustainably, and the whaling fleets moved from one area to another as the local populations of whales were depleted. The focus had been on the relatively easy-to-catch right, bowhead, sperm, gray and humpback whales. The faster-swimming balaenopterids (especially blue and fin whales) had so far evaded capture from sailing or rowing boats — but that was soon to change.

In 1863, Norwegian whaler Svend Foyn mounted an explosive harpoon gun on a steam ship and the era of modern whaling began. The faster steam ships could hunt down blue or fin whales and the explosive harpoon could disable and kill a whale (relatively) quickly before it was lost. Starting in the north-eastern Atlantic, catches of these whales declined around Norway, then around Iceland and then progressively further south as the fleets pursued the profits that came from hunting whales. Whaling of these species was mostly coastally based and land stations were built in many places along the coasts of Europe, North and South America and Africa to process whales brought ashore. Remains of some of these whaling stations can still be found today, for example at Bunavoneader on the Hebridean Isle of Harris.

In the early 1900s, modern whaling had expanded as far southwards as South Georgia in the South Atlantic and several land stations, including Grytviken, Leith Harbour, Husvik and Stromness, were built there to take advantage of the abundance of whales in the vicinity. Importantly, the highly productive and hitherto unexploited waters of the Southern Ocean were now within reach. In 1926, the first factory ship with a stern slipway up which the whales could be hauled on board sailed to Antarctica. These floating factories could process whales far more efficiently than a shore-based station, and whaling could continue unimpeded on the high seas for many months.

ABOVE Scrimshaw on a sperm whale tooth of the whaling ship "Pacific", which operated out of Hobart, Australia in the 1840s and 1850s. Three whale catcher boats are hunting a sperm whale in the foreground.

LEFT A bowhead whale being speared with harpoons by early whalers in the Arctic Sea. Engraving by A. M. Fournier after E. Traviès.

MIDDLE The ruins of the whaling station at Leith Harbour on the island of South Georgia are a reminder of the beginnings of industrial-scale whaling in the Southern Ocean, which persisted until the 1960s.

BOTTOM Modern Japanese factory ship with minke whales being winched on board up the slipway.

RIGHT Commercial catches of whales in the Southern Hemisphere in the twentieth century.

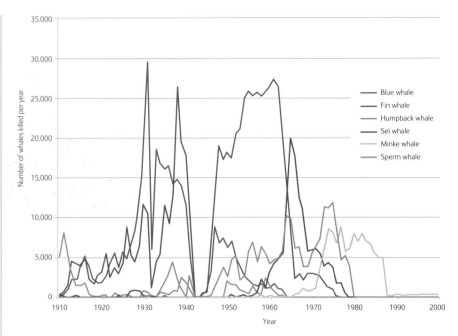

RIGHT Commercial catches of whales in the Southern Hemisphere in the twentieth century.

By 1930, most of the world's whaling was concentrated in the Southern Ocean, and over the next four decades around 1.5 million whales were taken from there. Whalers first targeted the largest balaenopterid, the blue whale, and then the progressively smaller fin whale and sei whale, as catches declined. Blue whale catches increased rapidly to a peak of almost 30,000 whales in 1930–1931 and then declined steadily, with a break during World War II, over the next 30 years. Fin whale catches overtook blue whales in the mid-1930s and stayed high until declining precipitately in the 1960s, when sei whales briefly became the whalers' focus in the absence of larger species. Large numbers of sperm whales and humpback whales were also taken. By the end of the 1960s, unrelenting catches had reduced the populations of these large whale species to levels far below those that could support commercial whaling. The demand for whale oil had also dwindled because of the wide availability of mineral oils, and from the mid-1970s the focus of Antarctic whaling turned to the much smaller minke whale, which was taken for meat.

Meanwhile, although whale populations had declined in the Antarctic, there was still a sufficient market for whale products (for example for making soap, cosmetics and margarine) for whaling to increase again in the Northern Hemisphere in the 1950s, 1960s and 1970s, mainly for sperm whales but also for fin, sei and minke whales. In addition to European and American whaling, modern whaling had also been developed by Japan in the North Pacific during the twentieth century. The unpalatable bottom line is that in the 70 years between 1910 and 1980, not far short of three million whales were hunted and killed for commercial purposes worldwide and the populations were reduced to a very small fraction of their pre-whaling abundance. There were no longer enough large whales left to hunt, and the days of industrial-scale whaling were over.

THE SHIFT FROM EXPLOITATION TO PROTECTION

Rachel Carson's 1962 book *Silent Spring*, which documented the negative effects of chemical pesticides on wildlife, especially birds (see also page 128), is seen by many as a catalyst for a grassroots awakening to the detrimental impact that humans have had on our planet. As part of overall changes in the relationship between humans and the rest of the environment, people gradually became more informed about whales and other cetaceans. They also became aware about the extent and effects of whaling through popular science articles such as 'The Last of the Great Whales' published in *Scientific American* in 1966 and the exploits of anti-whaling activists. The devastating impacts of whaling in the middle decades of the twentieth century grew to be, in some quarters, symbolic of human disregard for the wider environment and became embodied in the 'Save the Whales' campaign to put a stop to whaling.

The International Whaling Commission (IWC) was established in 1946 to implement the International Convention for the Regulation of Whaling, the purpose of which is 'to provide for the proper conservation of whale stocks and thus make possible the orderly development of the whaling industry'. Initial attempts by the IWC to manage whaling were totally ineffective, as demonstrated by the continued over-exploitation of whale populations throughout the world. The measure used to regulate catches continued to be the blue whale unit (BWU), established pre-IWC in 1931 as a market control to limit the supply of oil. One BWU equalled one blue whale, two fin whales, two and a half humpback whales or six sei whales. The IWC tried to limit catches by restricting the length of the Antarctic whaling season, which led to over-investment in whaling fleets in attempts to catch as many whales as quickly as possible. There was no attempt to manage whaling so that catches of whales were sustainable for each species.

It took the 1972 UN Conference on the Human Environment in Stockholm to spur the IWC towards rational management of whaling and, in 1974, catch limits for individual species were set for the first time based on the principle of sustainable catches. However, application of the new management procedure was problematic for a number of reasons, including lack of reliable data, a tendency for catch limits to vary widely from one year to the next, and the use of supplementary rules such as assuming that a long period of approximately constant catches meant that such catches were sustainable.

As a result, and because of the growing environmental movement, calls for a halt on whaling of all species steadily grew during the 1970s. The movement to ban whaling culminated in 1982 with the IWC's adoption of a 'pause in commercial whaling', popularly known as the moratorium, which came into effect in 1986. Subsistence whaling by indigenous peoples, for example bowhead whales taken by the Alaskan Inuit, was still allowed but catch limits for commercial whaling were all set to zero.

Was this the end of commercial whaling? It was not. IWC regulations allow member governments to object formally to any decision and to issue special permits to their whalers to take whales for research purposes, so-called 'scientific whaling'. Currently, under these loopholes in the rules, Norway and Iceland take whales under objection in the North Atlantic and Japan issues research permits to take whales in the North Pacific and Antarctic, although special permit whaling in the Antarctic was declared illegal by the International Court of Justice in 2014.

The approximately 1,000 whales taken annually today, mostly minke whales but also fin, sei and Bryde's whales, are a very small fraction of the average 50,000 taken per year in the heyday of modern whaling. The numbers currently taken are also small relative to the estimated sizes of the populations targeted and pose little or no risk to the conservation of the species; in other words, the whaling is sustainable. But 1,000 whales a year is still a lot of whales. For large sections of society, whaling has become unacceptable. An important concern is the welfare of the whales; killing a whale is an uncertain activity and death can never be instantaneous, even under optimal circumstances. The issue for many people is not conservation but complete protection; for them whaling has no place in the modern world.

The debate about whaling will no doubt continue, but today there are several other arguably much more important pressures on cetacean populations throughout the world, some of which raise serious conservation concerns; these are considered in Chapter 8.

NON-CONSUMPTIVE USES OF WHALES

The 1970s and 1980s saw the development of the vision that humans could, indeed should, be using whales for 'non-consumptive' purposes, rather than killing them. This term encompassed the ideas that cetaceans were important components of marine ecosystems that should be studied using benign (non-lethal) methods (Chapters 2 to 6) and that human 'use' should be focused on recreation, such as whale-watching, and drawing on their universal appeal to facilitate education about the environment of which we are all a part. The principle that non-consumptive use is as important as consumptive use was incorporated into the Convention on Biological Diversity in 2004.

Today, human encounters with whales and other cetaceans are largely recreational, including observing them in captive facilities purpose-built for public display, watching them from shore or boat in their natural surroundings, or even more interactive activities such as swimming with captive or wild animals, and in some locations feeding wild animals.

Keeping whales and dolphins in captivity had early beginnings in the nineteenth century, but the first marine park keeping dolphins opened in Florida in the 1930s; by the 1960s the business of displaying cetaceans started to develop more intensively. The most popular species were initially beluga whales, killer whales and bottlenose dolphins, but a wide variety of dolphins and small whales are now kept in captivity

for display. At first, animals had to be captured in the wild and brought into captivity, a difficult, traumatic and often fatal experience for the animals involved, but captive breeding programmes were developed in some marine parks to minimize the need to 'restock'.

There has long been a vigorous debate about keeping cetaceans in captivity, as part of more general arguments about the justification for zoos of any kind. Opponents argue that confining cetaceans to tanks is cruel because their lives are restricted in drastic ways; they cannot range freely as in the wild, they lack the stimulation of their natural environment, their social interactions are disrupted or destroyed, and they are prone to disease and early death; it is unethical to keep such highly developed and obviously intelligent animals restrained for human entertainment and company profit. Proponents argue that the benefits of research and education outweigh these negative aspects: some research, such as investigation of diving physiology (Chapter 4), experiments to measure hearing thresholds and how cetaceans use sound socially or for catching fish, can most effectively or only be done in captivity; most people will never get the opportunity to observe whales in their natural environment and keeping animals in captivity helps to teach the public about whales and the importance of protecting both them and the wider environment.

There may be signs that the tide is turning against keeping whales in captivity. Under pressure from animal rights activists and bad publicity causing a decline in business, the US company SeaWorld announced the end of its captive breeding programme for killer whales in early 2016, signalling a beginning of the end of keeping this species in captivity in SeaWorld marine parks. However, there are many other marine parks around the world, including in countries where there is little or no regulation, where cetaceans of various species are kept and sometimes bred. Animals also continue to be taken from the wild to stock such display facilities. It remains to be seen whether or not the decision by SeaWorld is significant in the ongoing debate about whether or not cetaceans should be kept in captivity.

Observing whales and other cetaceans in their natural habitats, commonly referred to as whale-watching, has become widespread and a major contribution to local economies worldwide as part of the general boom in wildlife tourism. From early beginnings watching gray whales off California in the 1950s, a comprehensive review found that in 2008, 13 million people participated in whale-watching activities in 119 countries, with a total economic value of three billion US dollars (USD). A study in Australia in 2011 estimated that the touristic value of a single whale over its lifetime ranged from around 30,000 Australian dollars (AUD) to more than one million AUD, depending on the population size and species of whale and the location. Clearly, whale-watching is big business.

Whale-watching operations around the world vary greatly in terms of focal species, scale, type of vessel (or land-based), etc. Many countries have legal or voluntary codes of conduct to which whale-watching operators should adhere to prevent adverse effects on the very animals that are intended to be seen in their natural conditions. Boat-based whale-watching may affect the animals being observed and the severity of any effects are likely to increase when activities are over-concentrated or unregulated. Natural behaviour such as feeding or socializing may be disturbed, animals may be driven away from favoured areas that are important to them, and continued disturbance may even cause decreases in survival or birth rates over a period of time. Long-term population effects are of most conservation concern. Sustainability is important for non-consumptive uses of whales, just as it is for consumptive uses.

RIGHT Cruise ship passengers are treated to a chance opportunity to observe a group of killer whales in the Gerlache Strait, Antarctica. In this encounter, the whales approached the vessel, which had slowed down in accordance with good practice guidelines.

In some circumstances, whale-watching operations can provide a platform for certain research activities. For example, pictures taken by tourists or researchers on board whale-watching boats may be useful for photo-identification studies (see page 55) or may provide information on foraging and feeding behaviour (Chapters 5 and 6). However, caution is needed to make sure that the research is not compromised by any effects of whale-watching operations on the behaviour of the whales being studied.

More interactive, and therefore more intrusive, than boat-based whale-watching are operations in which people get in the water with animals in enclosures or the open sea (known as 'swim-with' activities), or feed them from either a boat or the land (known as provisioning). Humans have interacted with dolphins in these ways for a long time but there has been a surge in these activities in recent decades.

Getting into the water to swim with dolphins is a popular activity, especially in warm-water locations, but the legality and control of such encounters varies greatly around the world. Swimming with dolphins in marine parks raises the same issues and concerns about keeping cetaceans in captivity as described above. In more natural conditions in the open sea, the animals are theoretically more in control of the encounters but, in cases where there is hands-on physical interaction, there are potential dangers of injury to both humans and dolphins, and serious injuries

BELOW A dwarf minke whale investigating a snorkeler being towed on a line behind a whale-watching vessel, Queensland, Australia.

ABOVE Feeding wild dolphins at Tangalooma Resort on Moreton Island, Queensland, Australia.

to swimmers have been documented. It is easy to forget that, as well as being graceful, fascinating creatures, whales and dolphins are large, wild and at times unpredictable animals.

Some 'swim-with' operations aim to avoid physical interaction; one example occurs at the Great Barrier Reef in Queensland. Snorkellers or divers hold onto a rope trailed behind a whale-watching boat and are towed through an area where dwarf minke whales occur during the Southern Hemisphere winter.

The control of activities in which fish are fed to dolphins also varies greatly. Concerns about these human-dolphin close interactions include the possibility of physical injury to both parties, the transmission of diseases and the dolphins becoming dependent on artificial feeding so that their ability to feed for themselves or care for their offspring is compromised. One example of such provisioning is the feeding of bottlenose dolphins at Tangalooma, Queensland, Australia. The dolphins arrive at the same time in the afternoon each day and position themselves in front of lines of tourists to be fed. When the fish have all been eaten, the dolphins depart to return the next day.

All these activities described above involve humans interacting with cetaceans for recreational purposes. But there are situations in which dolphins cooperate with local fishers to mutual benefit. One place where this interaction has been well-documented is Laguna in Brazil. One particular social group of bottlenose dolphins

drives mullet towards the waiting fishermen; the dolphins then signal when nets should be cast and feed off fish that are escaping from the nets. The dolphins thus benefit from the fishing activity, and without the aid of the dolphins the fish would not be caught. In other similar situations, the interaction may be better described as commensal, with dolphins perhaps enhancing fishing success but mainly feeding off fishery discards.

This chapter has documented the shift in the way that humans view and interact with whales and other cetaceans. From early utilization and hunting, through centuries of devastating commercial over-exploitation; in the last few decades whales and other cetaceans have come to be recognized as remarkable animals of ecological importance (see page 93) as well as being seen by large sections of society as creatures of wonder to be nurtured. Like so many other aspects of our lives, this shift happened rather rapidly over the last few decades. It has occurred in parallel with, indeed partly because of, our increased understanding of the biology of whales. The more our knowledge of whales increases, the greater our understanding of their biology and ecology, and the more we can value their place in our world.

ABOVE Fishermen and bottlenose dolphins work together in Laguna, Brazil to catch fish to their mutual benefit.

CHAPTER 8

Changing oceans

FOLLOWING THE END OF THE ERA of industrial-scale whaling and the changes in public attitudes towards whales and the environment in general, what does the future hold for whales as we move into a world affected more and more by the impact of human activities on our planet? In this final chapter, we consider current pressures on whales, dolphins and porpoises around the world and contemplate the threats that they face from changes in the decades to come.

INTERACTIONS WITH FISHERIES

Of all human activities, fishing has arguably had the greatest impact on the marine environment. Chemical isotope analysis (similar to the method used to investigate whale diet – see pages 86–87) and fish bones found in middens (waste dumps) show that humans have been eating fish since the Stone Age around 40,000 years ago. Such early fishing could have had little environmental impact, but during the last millennium fishing developed steadily as the human population grew. Methods became more sophisticated and sailing ships became more substantial and thus able to catch more fish and to travel further afield to catch them. By the sixteenth century European fleets were crossing the Atlantic to fish cod on the Grand Banks off Newfoundland.

Industrialization in Europe and America led to an expansion of fisheries; produce from the seas at that time seemed boundless. In 1884, in evidence to a British Royal Commission, TH Huxley said: 'I believe, then, that ... probably all the great sea fisheries are inexhaustible; that is to say, that nothing we do seriously affects the numbers of fish.' Between 1840 and 1860 the population of the USA had almost doubled to 32 million and fish had started to be caught for animal feed, and to make oil and fertilizer, as well as for human consumption. The change from sailing boats to steam ships in the 1870s made fishing much more efficient because the ships were more powerful and were not reliant on the wind.

Following the end of World War II, there were further developments in fishing gear and in markets for food fish and fish meal, which saw a large expansion of distant water fleets throughout the world. Since 1950, the global harvest of fish, shellfish and

OPPOSITE A bowhead whale surfacing surrounded by pieces of melting ice. Bowheads are known to be among the longest-lived mammals, living for more than 200 years.

other marine produce has increased from 20 million tonnes to more than 120 million tonnes, with the increase since around 1990 coming from aquaculture, including fish and shellfish farming, and fish fattening farms. Wild fish stocks have been fully or over-exploited for a quarter of a century. The removal of all this fish biomass over a long period of time means that ocean ecosystems today are very different from the pristine environments in which whales previously lived.

ENTANGLEMENT AND INCIDENTAL MORTALITY

The most evident and direct way in which fisheries impact whales is by entangling them in fishing gear. Some whales may be released unharmed, but the very large majority are killed. This incidental mortality, or bycatch, occurs globally but estimating the magnitude of the problem is difficult, primarily because information from the developing world is sparse. A crude estimate of the number of marine mammals killed annually has been made by extrapolating bycatch rates in USA fisheries to the rest of the world based on the number of fishing vessels listed by the United Nations (UN) Food and Agriculture Organization. This figure, for the mid-1990s, was more than a quarter of a million animals per year and is almost certainly an underestimate. A recent study found that 61 of the 75 currently recognized odontocete species and 13 of 14 mysticete species were known to be caught in fishing gear. Bycatch is clearly the greatest single direct threat to cetaceans today.

The main fishing gear responsible for cetacean bycatch is the gillnet, a net made of very thin plastic line and set either on the seabed or as a driftnet at the surface. Bycatch in gillnets is the primary reason why the baiji (the Yangtze river dolphin) is now functionally extinct, and is the sole reason for the precipitous decline of the vaquita (the Gulf of California porpoise) to a few tens of animals.

For some species, bycatch has been greatly reduced from previously very high numbers. Hundreds of thousands of spinner and spotted dolphins were once killed in

RIGHT The vaquita is the most endangered cetacean in the world; as few as 30 animals are thought to remain in its restricted range in the northern Gulf of California, Mexico. It is killed in illegal gillnets set for totoaba, also a *Critically Endangered* species, to supply a lucrative demand in China for the swim bladders of the fish, which are mistakenly believed to have medicinal properties.

purse seine nets for yellowfin tuna in the eastern tropical Pacific Ocean in the 1960s. Various management measures introduced over the years, including the USA Marine Mammal Protection Act in 1972 and the setting up of the International Dolphin Conservation Program in 1992, have now reduced those numbers to hundreds per year. A UN ban on high seas driftnets in 1992 led to a large reduction in mortality of northern right whale dolphins in the North Pacific from around 20,000 to hundreds per year.

A concern in some situations is that bycatch in a fishery will turn into direct activity to catch cetaceans. This has occurred in Peru, where dusky dolphins previously taken as bycatch are now actively hunted for food. Some believe that fishing nets that can result in bycatch of minke whales in Korean waters may be set partially to increase the chances of catching these whales because they are so valuable.

Some species of the larger baleen whales also have a tendency to become entangled in the lines and ropes of static fishing gear, including traps and pots. North Atlantic right whales become entangled in such gear in their feeding areas off the coasts of the USA and Canada. Based on an analysis of wounds and scars on photo-identified animals, more than 50 per cent of the population is estimated to have been entangled at least twice in their lifetime, with an annual rate of entanglement of 15 per cent. With a population of around 500 animals, such entanglement is clearly of great concern even if only a small proportion result in death.

DEPREDATION

Some cetaceans interact with fisheries by attempting to take fish directly from fishing gear, a behaviour known as depredation. This reduces the catch rate for the fishers through damaged or lost fish and can lead to damage to the gear itself. The result can be highly detrimental economically to fishers, who may take measures to

BELOW A North Atlantic right whale migrates southwards off the coast of Florida, USA trailing a large quantity of fishing line. This whale was fortunate — a team of biologists managed to disentangle it from the lines.

RIGHT Killer whales surface adjacent to a trawler near San Juan Island in Washington State, USA. Killer whales and sperm whales can take fish from nets and lines (known as depredation), potentially causing a lot of damage to the catch.

scare the whales or dolphins away from the fishing gear, and even resort to trying to kill them. It may also potentially lead to animals becoming entangled in the gear they are depredating (see above).

Some nets targeted are deployed by artisanal (small-scale traditional) fisheries in coastal areas. The species most known to interact with these fisheries is the bottlenose dolphin, present in coastal waters in many parts of the world and well-known for its inventiveness in foraging behaviour (see page 90). In Italian waters a study found that bottlenose and striped dolphins depredated two-thirds of gillnets and trammel nets (nets similar to gillnets with an inner small mesh net sandwiched between two outer larger mesh nets and set on the seabed) in artisanal fisheries.

Of the larger whales, the main perpetrators of depredation are killer whales and sperm whales, which take fish from long lines, a fishing gear in which baited hooks are suspended at intervals along a very long main line set near the surface to catch tuna, for example, or close to the seabed to catch demersal species and flatfish. Sperm whales have been recorded depredating longlines off South America and around sub-Antarctic islands (lines set for toothfish), in the Gulf of Alaska (sablefish and halibut) and off Norway and Greenland (halibut and cod). Killer whales depredate some of these same fisheries in the Southern Hemisphere and the Gulf of Alaska. Pilot whales and false killer whales are also known to depredate longline fisheries targeting swordfish and tuna.

INDIRECT INTERACTIONS

A less obvious interaction between whales and fisheries is that they are, in a sense, competitors for resources. It has been proposed that reducing whale numbers will reduce predation and help fish stocks recover so that they are more productive and generate higher catches. However, the overlap in whale prey and fisheries catches depends on the species. The baleen whales of the world primarily eat krill but also fish in some cases. Sperm whales and other deep diving species of toothed whale

LEFT Biologists examine the stomach content of a sperm whale which had died after swallowing 17 kg (37½ lbs) of plastics, including plastic bags used for rubbish or construction materials, plastic packaging covers, ropes and pieces of nets.

mainly eat squid. The many species of dolphin and porpoise eat both fish and squid. In fact, the main predators of fish are other fish; seals and seabirds are also major fish consumers. So fish prey that might be left uneaten by removing whale predators would likely be consumed by other predators.

One can also consider the impact that fishing has had on whales through removal of enormous quantities of fish biomass over centuries and the inevitable changes in fish assemblages. With the exception of some areas in the Mediterranean Sea, where it has been proposed that fishing has severely reduced the prey available for cetaceans, such as the common dolphin, there is little evidence that whales have suffered from changes to ecosystems caused by fishing. Of greater potential concern are the effects of global warming, which are discussed below.

CHEMICAL POLLUTION

Chemical pollution in the ocean can take a variety of forms, ranging from plastics to chemical contaminants. Some pollutants are unintentionally discarded and end up in the ocean; others are dumped either legally or illegally. As a threat to marine life, chemical pollution is particularly difficult to deal with. Most such pollutants enter the sea from sources on land or from ships but they can become widely dispersed and very difficult to clean up.

Today plastic is everywhere: plastic bags, styrofoam or plastic cups, plastic bottles, plastic toys. In the North Pacific, there are several vortices of currents, the centres of which tend to have still water and accumulate particularly high concentrations of debris. Plastics have become a particular problem for some marine predators because they can be mistaken for food and, if eaten in sufficient quantity, may lead to death.

Some examples illustrate the problem. In August 2014, a young female sei whale was found dead in Chesapeake Bay along the east coast of America – a broken DVD case was identified as the cause of death. In 2013, a sperm whale washed up on Spain's southern coast, and an astonishing 17 kg (37½ lbs) of plastic, including

RIGHT A beluga whale swims under ice in the Arctic Circle, northern Russia. Belugas inhabiting river estuaries contain particularly high levels of contaminants, but relatively high levels have also been found in animals which live in the open sea.

clothing hangers, ice cream containers and plastic sheeting, were found in its stomach. In 2016, 13 sperm whales stranded along the North Sea coast of Germany, four of which were found to have large amounts of plastic in their stomachs including a 13-m (43-ft)-long shrimp fishing net, a plastic car engine cover and part of a plastic bucket. All these whales were found because they washed up on the beach. But most whales die at sea, so it is difficult to know the extent of the problem of ingestion of large pieces of plastic by whales.

Microplastics are small plastic particles in the environment that are less than one millimetre (0.04 in) in size. They come from cosmetics, clothing, and industrial processes; they may be either manufactured at this size (like the beads found in facewash or toothpaste) or broken down from larger plastics. It is currently unclear how whales and dolphins may be affected by microplastics, but one concern is that their high surface area helps to concentrate synthetic organic chemical compounds such as persistent organic pollutants (POPs), which may then be ingested.

POPs are human-made chemicals that are not readily biodegradable and so persist in the environment and accumulate in food webs. In the late 1960s they hit the headlines when Rachel Carson alerted the world to the potential impact of pesticides in her book *Silent Spring*. In 2001, the Stockholm Convention on Persistent Organic Pollutants came into effect 'to protect human health and the environment from persistent organic pollutants'. POPs are organochlorine (and similar compounds in the halogen chemical group) pesticides, which are highly fat soluble and so accumulate in the tissues, particularly in the blubber of whales and other marine mammals. Top predators such as belugas and killer whales that feed at upper levels of the food web are particularly likely to accumulate large toxin burdens due to biomagnification (i.e. an increase in concentration from one trophic level to another). Many POPs have been banned, including the polychlorinated biphenyls (PCBs) banned in the USA (in

LEFT Whales are at risk from accidental oil spills. They are also affected by sounds used in seismic surveys to locate subsea deposits of oil and gas.

1979), the UK (1981) and the European Union (1987), and levels of POPs in many marine species have been slowly declining since then.

However, a study published in 2016 found excessively high PCB levels were still present in some European cetaceans, particularly killer whales, bottlenose dolphins and striped dolphins. High PCB levels can cause a suite of problems, disrupting hormones (the natural signalling molecules that the body uses to control biological processes), decreasing fertility, and causing deformities, abnormal behaviour and a weakened immune system. Female whales, dolphins and porpoises can pass on a large proportion of their PCB burden via the womb and in their milk to their first-born calves, which may be born with health problems or even die. Adult males accumulate their PCB burden throughout life and typically have the highest levels of PCBs.

The best-known example of these issues comes from the population of around 500 belugas that live in the St Lawrence Estuary in Canada. Individuals in this population have very high pollutant concentrations in their tissues compared with belugas that live in the less contaminated waters of the Arctic. A study begun in 1982 found that only one in five females was pregnant or had recently calved (compared with two-thirds of female belugas in the Arctic). In addition, 18 of 45 belugas examined had cancerous tumours. Some have gone so far as to say that dead belugas should be considered toxic waste because they exceed the PCB threshold for industrial toxic waste!

POPs are not static but can transfer in the air from industrialized to non-industrialized regions via cycles of volatization and condensation called global distillation. This is the same process by which chemicals are distilled or purified in a laboratory. A chemical is vaporized at high temperature and then travels to an area of lower temperature, where it condenses. In addition there may be slower degradation of chemicals in cooler climates. However, with fewer POPs now being produced, one problem is determining where new sources are coming from. Dredging of PCB-laden rivers and estuaries or leakage from old landfills are possible sources. To reduce the effects of PCBs on marine predators, new initiatives are needed to limit PCB mobilization in marine sediments and regulate demolition of PCB-containing precast buildings such as tower blocks built in the 1950s to 1960s.

Oil spills can have immediate adverse effects on marine life. It was previously thought that the most severe impacts were on animals whose fur could be compromised by the oil, but oil spills can also affect whales and dolphins when they eat prey that has become contaminated, breathe in fumes, or swim through oil. In the longer term there can be problems through toxicity or habitat degradation. In the first year after the 1989 *Exxon Valdez* oil spill off Alaska, a group of 'transient' killer whales, known as the AT1 pod, lost 41 per cent of its animals and apparently became sterile. The more recent 2011 Deepwater Horizon oil spill in the Gulf of Mexico also appeared to cause severe ill health in the Louisiana bottlenose dolphin population. Although there were relatively few (101) cetacean carcasses recovered following the spill, the true death toll could be 50 times higher because the probability of finding carcasses is very small due to sinking, decaying, drifting or being scavenged.

SOUND

We normally do not think of sound as a form of pollution, but the UN Convention on the Law of the Sea defines the introduction of energy into the ocean as a form of pollution if it causes deleterious effects. Sound is a form of energy and, in the case of sonar-caused strandings of beaked whales, it can definitely harm and kill whales.

SHIPS

The first alarm about the effects of sound on whales was raised in 1971. Scientists had just learnt about the low-frequency songs of whales and used sound propagation modelling to estimate the range over which whales might hear one another. The navies of the world have spent billions of pounds studying how sound travels in the sea, but this may not be intuitive to humans who are only familiar with sound in air. Under optimal propagation conditions in the deep ocean, the models predicted that the 20 Hz calls of fin whales would have been detectable at ranges of 5,600 km (3,480 miles) in the pre-industrial ocean. However, there are so many motorized ships in the ocean today that their noise reduces the range of fin whale calls to less than 1,000 km (620 miles) in optimal propagation, and only about 80 km (50 miles) under poor sound propagation.

We now know that these fin whale sounds are produced by adult males during the breeding season. If males use these sounds to attract females, then the reduction in range of communication caused by shipping noise could disrupt their reproduction, especially after hundreds of thousands of fin whales were killed by whaling in the twentieth century (see Chapter 7), decimating the population size, and probably increasing the typical separation distance between males and females. The issue of concern here is that shipping noise might mask the calls of a male, reducing the capability of a female to find or select a mate. If noise did disrupt the mating system,

it could harm the recovery of endangered whale populations without harming any individual animals.

A whale should easily be able to hear the sound of an oncoming ship, and some species such as minke whales are known to move away as a ship approaches. Ship noise has been shown to disrupt the behaviour of foraging beaked whales more than 5 km (3 miles) away. Prolonged disturbance caused by multiple passing ships could interfere with critical behaviours such as foraging, and may impact growth and ultimately reproduction (see Chapters 3 and 5).

However, some whales do not respond to the noise of an approaching ship, perhaps because they do not sense the potential danger, and it is well-known that some species of smaller cetacean, such as the common dolphin, may actively swim towards ships. If a whale is actually struck by a ship, this is likely to inflict serious injury and can result in the death of the whale. Whales can be struck by all kinds of vessels from large ocean going transport ships to fast ferries and even whale-watching boats. Large whales are most often the casualty but all species are potentially at risk. It is difficult to know the extent of the problem because for every recorded ship strike incident there must be many more that go undetected. Ship strikes are believed to be a particular problem for fin whales in the Mediterranean, which has some of the busiest shipping lanes in the world.

Whales that have favoured habitat which is crossed by busy shipping lanes thus face a dilemma. They need to respond to ships to avoid collision, but if they move away too far or for too long, this may also have adverse consequences on their foraging success, growth or reproduction.

The species most seriously impacted by ship strikes is the North Atlantic right whale, which inhabits the busy waters of the eastern seaboard of North America. More than one-third of known right whale deaths are a result of ship strikes, one incident a year. This may not sound like much but with a population of around 500 animals and entanglement in fishing gear also a source of mortality (see above), any additional deaths are a threat to the survival and recovery of this endangered

RIGHT Acoustic buoys listening for North Atlantic right whales in Massachusetts Bay, one of the busiest shipping lanes off the east coast of the USA. Shipping traffic in the area is alerted to whale detections so that ships can slow down to reduce the risk of fatal strikes to these endangered whales.

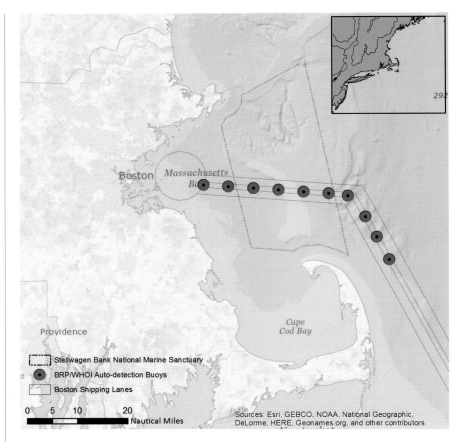

species. Measures to reduce the number of collisions have included modifying the ship traffic lanes to avoid areas of high whale density in the Bay of Fundy, Canada and in waters off the city of Boston. In the latter, a real-time whale alert system for mariners has been installed in which automated acoustic stations listen for right whale calls and send direct alerts of any whale detections to ship captains, who can then reduce speed and increase lookout activities to avoid hitting a whale (see page 131).

SONAR

One source of anthropogenic sound (sound arising from human activities) has been shown to actually kill whales. In 1998, a naval sonar exercise was associated with an unusual kind of mass stranding of beaked whales along the coast of Greece. Mass strandings of whales have been recorded for millennia, but they usually involve one group of animals all stranding together at the same time. The Greek stranding was atypical in that it involved 12 Cuvier's beaked whales stranding over two days over 38 km (24 miles) of coastline, with individual whales separated on average by 3.5 km (2.2 miles). This was particularly unusual because beaked whales usually inhabit the deep sea far from land, A search for potential causes revealed a naval sonar exercise that took place in the area during the same days. Naval sonar is intense enough (and sound travels far enough) that this is likely to be the only activity whose effects might be expected to manifest themselves over tens of kilometres in just a few hours.

Since then, global analyses of beaked whale strandings have identified one to two dozen cases of atypical strandings with varying evidence of association with naval sonar exercises. Some cases involve whales with symptoms of decompression sickness, probably caused by disruption of normal diving behaviour (see Chapter 4). It is now recognized that sonar does disrupt the deep diving behaviour of beaked whales; changes that at their most extreme lead to decompression symptoms and/or lethal stranding. There is some evidence that other species and other sound sources may be involved in similar kinds of strandings.

MARINE ENERGY

Ports and tourism have long been drivers of coastal development, but the continual search for new sources of energy has been a primary driver for building offshore structures such as oil and gas platforms, and wind farms. In the Gulf of Mexico, there are many thousands of offshore structures, and up to 27,000 abandoned oil and gas wells add to the risk of pollution from oil spills. In 2015 there were 184 active oil rigs in the North Sea, with an expanding development of windfarms.

However, when one considers the impact of noise, it is the seismic surveys used by industry to prospect below the sea floor for oil and gas deposits that are of greatest concern. Large seismic survey ships tow arrays of sound sources called airguns that direct intense sound energy downwards to detect echoes from deposits deep below the sea floor. The sound from airguns also propagates horizontally far from the arrays, where it can disturb marine life. There is evidence that the sound from seismic surveys can reduce the catch of fish by commercial fishermen over tens of kilometres, and can disrupt foraging and other behaviour of marine mammals. For example, one study in the Mediterranean Sea found that fin whales altered their calling behaviour when a 10-day seismic survey started, appeared to move away over the next three days, and did not return for two weeks after the survey ended. Similar studies of harbour porpoise in the North Sea have shown that they moved away to distances of 5–10 km (3–6 miles) at the onset of a seismic survey but then that distance reduced just a few hours after the survey started.

Some European countries have made a major commitment to develop marine renewable energy resources to reduce the amount of CO_2 released into the atmosphere. The operation of windfarms poses little environmental threat, except perhaps to seabirds in some locations. Their presence may even benefit some marine predators; for example, seals have been found to use these structures to forage, perhaps because they may act as attractors for their fish prey. However the construction of windfarms involves driving piles into the sea floor, which produces intense noises. A study listening to the sounds made by porpoises has found that these sounds decreased as far away as 20 km (12½ miles) from where piling was occurring, implying that porpoises may be driven away a considerable distance by the noise of the piling. If porpoises avoid the area around sources of piling for the entire period of construction, they may be excluded from favoured areas for many months. A primary concern about this kind of marine construction, therefore, is that it may reduce the habitat available to marine mammal populations and have negative consequences while it is taking place.

CLIMATE CHANGE

Climate change is not a new phenomenon. Over millions of years, changes in the Earth's climate have provided important forces shaping the evolution of life on our planet. However, the last 100 years have seen a rate of increase in CO_2 release and global warming that seem unprecedented in the Earth's history.

Average ocean temperatures are forecast by climate models to rise by 3–4°C by the end of the twenty-first century, with rates of warming expected to be even greater in polar waters. Global warming will lead to a largely ice-free Arctic Ocean, and to changes in ocean circulation and ocean acidification. All of these will have profound effects on the oceans' food webs and species distribution. Some of the likely effects of these changes on different species have been investigated to predict which might be the winners and losers in the changing oceans. For about half the whale species, immediate effects seem to be small or well within the ability of the whales to compensate for by shifting their ranges. Effects will be felt most profoundly by those species with narrow ecological ranges. This includes ice-dependent species such as beluga and narwhal, which track the seasonal changes of Arctic sea ice for both food and shelter from predation. Inuit hunters tell of encountering killer whales more frequently and further north nowadays. They report watching them hunt narwhals and belugas in ice free waters where the slow-moving whales have

BELOW Narwhals swimming off Baffin Island, Nunavut, Canada. Arctic cetaceans such as narwhals are particularly likely to suffer as the climate continues to warm and the sea ice melts.

less chance of escape from the killer whales' sustained and coordinated attacks. Thus, killer whales may benefit from warming seas by gaining more access to prey, whereas beluga and narwhals will experience increased predation pressure.

Some large whales, such as humpback and right whales, migrate thousands of kilometres each year from warm tropical waters where they give birth and mate to cooler polar waters where they feed (see pages 40 and 60–62). Sea ice loss in the Arctic and Antarctic is likely to affect the availability and abundance of the whales' currently preferred prey of zooplankton and small fish. Less food or a change in quality of food could have marked effects on the whales' ability to fatten up and lay down sufficient resources for the months of fasting as they travel to and from the breeding areas. Good body condition is crucial for female whales to breed and suckle a calf. Southern right whales off Brazil have been found to produce fewer calves after a bad feeding season in the Antarctic when there was less winter sea ice and krill was less abundant. Some humpback whales in the South Pacific seem to be shortening the distance they travel each year by exploiting food resources they encounter in southern Chile en route to the Antarctic. Humpback and fin whales have been arriving earlier at their feeding areas in the Gulf of St Lawrence, Canada at a rate of one day per year over the last 30 years in response to rising sea temperatures and the earlier break up of sea ice, which are believed to trigger the earlier onset of the spring bloom and subsequent availability of their prey. Thus, some whales appear able to exploit new opportunities that can arise from changes in prey availability.

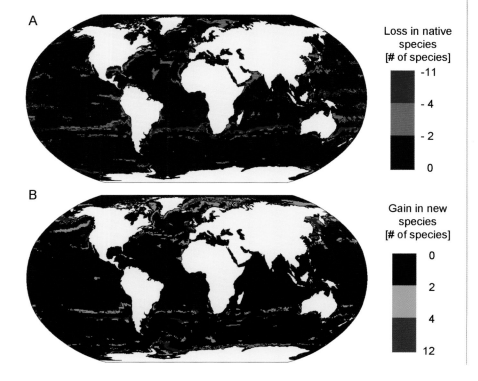

A

Loss in native
species
[# of species]

-11

- 4

- 2

0

B

Gain in new
species
[# of species]

0

2

4

12

LEFT Projected effects of climate change on cetacean species richness from the 1990s to the 2040s.

A much less understood consequence of the atmospheric increase in CO_2 and ocean warming is the resulting increase in ocean acidification and its effects on species at the base of marine food webs. At particular risk are calcifying organisms such as some plankton and many larval stages of fish and squid. Some species of whales, particularly sperm, pilot and beaked whales, specialize in hunting deep-water squid. Experiments have shown that squid embryos grow more slowly and have much higher mortality rates when exposed to water temperature and acidification levels forecasted by climate models. Increased mortality and reduced growth rates will affect the abundance and availability of squid to higher predators such as whales. How ocean acidification will affect complex marine ecosystems in future remains to be seen, but its effects on key components of the marine food webs and resulting cascading effects could be substantial and irreversible.

Reduced sea ice extent and warming waters offer opportunities to some whales. Warmer water species such as common dolphins or the tropical Bryde's whales can expand their ranges polewards. Such distributional shifts either may lead to range expansion or at least may allow warm-water species to compensate for losing existing tropical habitat that becomes less suitable because of further increasing temperatures. Cold-water species have limited options to shift ranges further north but reduced sea ice cover can create new movement pathways. In 2010, bowhead whales from the Atlantic and Pacific met, probably for the first time since the onset of the last ice age around 10,000 years ago, when the Arctic North-West Passage became sufficiently ice-free allowing whales from the two ocean basins to mix and mingle on the same feeding ground.

Gray whales in the North Pacific have recovered from intense whaling in the nineteenth century (see Chapter 7) to around 20,000 animals, but they disappeared from the entire North Atlantic in the early eighteenth century; whether this was a result of hunting or due to environmental factors is unclear. However, in 2010, sightings of a gray whale in the Mediterranean Sea made big waves in the media and amongst the scientific community. Another gray whale was then photographed in the South Atlantic off Namibia in 2013. It is most likely that the Mediterranean and Namibian gray whales originated from the North Pacific having taken one of two possible routes via the ice-free Arctic sea ways, either the North-West (Canadian) or the Northern (Russian) Passages.

However, ice-free waterways and reducing ice cover also open the Arctic to a potentially sharp increase in vessel traffic for commerce and recreation as well as resource exploitation, such as drilling for oil and gas, deep ocean mining and fishing. These activities bring with them added risks from ship strikes (particularly for slow-moving bowhead and right whales), oil and chemical spills, noise pollution from increased vessel traffic and seismic exploration, as well as undesirable interactions with fisheries by increasing net entanglement risk or competition for prey. Thus, the main threats to whales posed by climate change are likely to be via the combined and cumulative effects of human activities.

CUMULATIVE EFFECTS

Humans have influenced the ocean in myriad ways and a global analysis of human impacts found that all marine ecosystems were exposed to at least nine different threats. Overfishing has changed whole ecosystems, fishing gear kills hundreds of thousands of marine mammals each year, thousands of types of chemicals are dumped into the oceans, ships cause noise pollution and strike and kill whales. Climate change is increasing the temperature and acidity of many ocean areas globally, stressing marine ecosystems. As predators at or near the top of food chains, whales are impacted by toxic chemical pollutants, especially those that concentrate up the food chain. The concentrations of pesticides and PCBs measured in the blubber of killer whales and some dolphin species exceed safe toxicity thresholds, affect immune and reproductive systems and may have effects on populations. Whales are heavily dependent on sound, and their sensitivity to noise means that elevated noise levels can affect behaviour and in extreme cases cause injury or even death. Changes in prey availability resulting from fishing or climate change can place additional stress on cetacean populations.

When a whale is exposed to multiple stressors, it is difficult to predict how the effects will interact. How the ecosystems on which whales depend may be affected is even more difficult to predict. Many ecosystems are stabilized such that they do

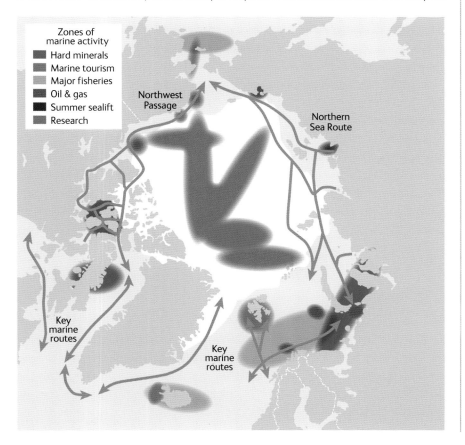

LEFT Human activities in the marine Arctic are diverse and include extraction of oil, gas and minerals, fisheries, marine shipping for commercial transport, recreation, research and military logistic activities (summer sealift).

not change state much as the stressors increase. However, they can reach a tipping point at which small changes in stressors can tip the ecosystem into an adverse state, from which recovery can be difficult. For example, the reduction in sea otter density caused by killer whale predation in some coastal areas of North America, described on page 93, could have been the tipping point that changed kelp forest ecosystems into 'urchin barrens' devoid of kelp.

The rapid demise of the Yangtze river dolphin – the baiji – to functional extinction can clearly be attributed to the cumulative effects of intense exploitation and degradation of the Yangtze river, where approximately 12 per cent of the world's human population lives. The baiji declined from around 6,000 individuals in the 1950s to around 300 in the 1980s as a consequence of construction of massive dams, hunting and, especially, bycatch in fishing nets. Many other species in the Yangtze still face the same threats and a similar fate to the baiji, including several indigenous fish species as well as another small cetacean, the Yangtze finless porpoise.

Two further examples serve to illustrate the potential for cumulative effects of human impacts. In 1990–1992, more than 1,000 striped dolphins were found dead in the Mediterranean Sea. The cause was identified as an outbreak of morbillivirus, and the total resulting mortality was probably very much higher. Morbillivirus outbreaks occur naturally (they also cause measles in humans, canine distemper in dogs, rinderpest in cattle, and phocine distemper in seals). In this striped dolphin outbreak however, it has been suggested that the animals were weakened both by an overall reduction in prey availability due to overfishing and by high levels of chemical contaminants compromising the immune system and this is why the virus took hold.

North Atlantic right whales are subject to multiple pressures, as described earlier in this chapter. They are vulnerable to ship strikes in their winter mating and calving areas off the south-eastern states of the USA and in their summer feeding areas off New England, and in the Bay of Fundy. They may become entangled in the lines of fishing gear (gillnets, traps and pots) in these same areas. Right whales may also be stressed by low-frequency noise generated by ships and they are vulnerable to reductions in the availability of their zooplankton prey as a result of changes in climate systems caused by ocean warming. Although formally assessing the way in which these effects interact is difficult, it seems likely that the lack of recovery from centuries of whaling and their current *Endangered* status is a result of the cumulative effects of these multiple stressors, despite management measures to reduce those impacts.

CONCLUSIONS

Whales, dolphins and porpoises occur in all climatic and ecological zones throughout the world. They have developed remarkable adaptations that enable them to feed, survive and reproduce in continental shelf or slope waters and in the deep oceans, in polar, temperate and tropical regions. Compared with terrestrial mammals they are large, well-insulated, efficient swimmers, have exceptional diving capabilities and use sound more than sight to navigate, hunt and communicate. Whales have evolved a way of life that takes advantage of stable, predictable marine environments. They invest a lot of resources in raising a single calf and there may be several years between births. To offset this slow rate of reproduction, they increase their lifetime reproductive output by being long-lived. Individuals of most species may live for several decades, and the bowhead whale may live to more than 200 years. However, these same adaptations that have seen whales become such a globally successful group of species are the reason they are so vulnerable to the effects of human activities. Their large size and thick layer of blubber made them the target of whaling over a period of 300 years in the seventeenth to twentieth centuries, and their slow rate of reproduction aided the decimation of their populations by the whaling industry.

The days of large-scale whaling are over and many populations have recovered well. However, others are still struggling at low numbers and the threat of whaling has been replaced by other human pressures that whales must cope with. Their need to breathe air means that cetaceans large and small are susceptible to being suffocated in fishing gear. Their blubber stores chemical pollutants that have been concentrated as they pass up the food chain, which can cause a range of physiological, behavioural and physical problems. Their reliance on sound as a primary sense makes them vulnerable to the noise made by shipping, construction of marine infrastructure and naval exercises. Climate warming adds additional uncertainty to the future prospects of whales. The challenges faced by whales, dolphins and porpoises now and in the coming decades are thus substantial and it will require considerable human effort to control our activities sufficiently to allow these remarkable species to prosper.

In spite of this, and noting that some species such as the Gulf of California vaquita and right whales in the Northern Hemisphere are in a very precarious state, there are reasons to be positive about the future. The desire for conservation of whales and the marine environment has never been stronger. Many countries around the world have legislation to protect whales, dolphins and porpoises, and there are several global and regional international organizations that have a focus on whale conservation, including the IWC that previously failed to halt destructive twentieth century whaling. Large numbers of people work for and support the many charitable organizations focused on protecting and conserving whales. There are also more researchers than ever before working to increase our knowledge and understanding of whales and their role in the varied marine environments they inhabit throughout the world. The better we understand the lives of whales, the better we will be able to inform decisions made about managing human influence on them.

Ultimately, the level of protection afforded to the natural environment is down to us, the public. Many people around the world from all walks of life and society now care deeply about whales, and take an active interest in their wellbeing. It is the politicians making policy and the managers implementing that policy who must take the decisions to regulate human activities that are harmful to whales and the environments they inhabit. Public support is vital to influence those politicians and managers to make the changes necessary for limiting our impact so that whale populations can recover and be maintained in healthy marine ecosystems.

Further information

FURTHER READING

Berta, A., Kovacs, K. and Sumich, J. L. (third edition, 2015), *Marine Mammals: Evolutionary Biology*, Elsevier.

Boyd, I. L., Bowen, W. D. and Iverson, S. J. (eds) (2010), *Marine Mammal Ecology and Conservation: A Handbook of Techniques*, Oxford University Press.

Carson, R., (new edition, 2000), *Silent Spring*, Penguin.

Castellini, M. A. and Mellish, J-A. (eds) (2015), *Marine Mammal Physiology: Requisites for Ocean Living*, CRC Press.

Cozzi, B., Huggenberger, S. and Oelschläger, H. (2016), *Anatomy of Dolphins: Insights into Body Structure and Function*, Elsevier.

Jefferson, T., Pitman, R. L. and Webber, M. A. (second edition, 2015), *Marine Mammals of the World: A Comprehensive Guide to Their Identification*, Elsevier.

Richardson, J. R., Greene, C. R. Jr., Malme, C. I. and Thomson, D. H. (1995), *Marine Mammals and Noise*, Elsevier.

Whitehead, H. and Rendell, L. (2014), *The Cultural Lives of Whales and Dolphins*, University of Chicago Press.

Wilson, B. and Wilson, A. (2006), *The Complete Whale-Watching Handbook: A Guide to Whales, Dolphins, and Porpoises of the World*, Voyageur Press.

Würsig, B., Thewissen, J. G. M. and Kovacs, K. M. (eds) (third edition, 2017), *Encyclopedia of Marine Mammals*, Elsevier/Academic Press.

WEBSITES

International Union for Conservation of Nature (IUCN) Red List of Threatened Species. www.iucn.org/resources/conservation-tools/iucn-red-list-threatened-species

International Whaling Commission (IWC). https://iwc.int

Sea Mammal Research Unit (SMRU). www.smru.st-andrews.ac.uk/

Society for Marine Mammalogy List of Marine Mammal Species and Subspecies. www.marinemammalscience.org/species-information/list-marine-mammal-species-subspecies/

Index

Acknowledgements

PICTURE CREDITS

p.4 By José Eugenio Gómez Rodríguez (Own work) [GFDL (http://www.gnu.org/copyleft/fdl.html) or CC BY 3.0 (http://creativecommons.org/licenses/by/3.0)], via Wikimedia Commons; pp.6, 8 top, 15 and 79 ©Mark Carwardine/naturepl.com; pp.8 bottom, 47, 54, 59 and 89 © Philip Hammond; pp.10, 19 bottom, 20, 38a,c,d, 55 top right and bottom left and 118 © Sonja Heinrich; p.12 ©Science Source/Science Photo Library; p.13 © Carl Zimmer; p.14 © Courtesy of Smithsonian Institution. Photo by A. Metallo; p.16 © P. A. Morin, K. M. Parsons, F. I. Archer, et al. 2015. *Mol. Ecol.*; p.19 top ©Juan Carlos Munoz/naturepl.com; p.21 top © DigiMorph.org/Rachel Racicot; bottom ©M/Watson/ardea.com; p.22 top ©WHOI Computerized Scanning and Imaging Facility. Reprinted with permission, D. R. Ketten, all rights reserved; p22 bottom ©Francois Gohier/ardea.com; p.24 ©Franco Banfi/Biosphoto/ardea.com; p.26 top © 2015, Wisniewska et al (2015) *eLife*; p.26 bottom By Kurzon (Own work) [CC BY-SA 3.0 (http://creativecommons.org/licenses/by-sa/3.0), via Wikimedia Commons; p.28 ©Steven Kazlowski/naturepl.com; p.30 ©Doug Perrine/naturepl.com; p.32 top Jordi Chias/naturepl.com; middle ©Carla Christie; bottom © Doc White/naturepl.com; p.33 Gabriel Barathieu via Wikimedia Commons; p.34 ©Richard Gerrish/Dreamstime.com; p.35 ©Francois Gohier/ardea.com; p.36 ©Deb Price, Dept. Conservation New Zealand; p.38 b ©Steve Dawson, NOAA; p.39 ©Southwest Fisheries Science Center, NOAA Fisheries Service; p.40 top © J.W. Durban, R. L.Pitman (2012) *Biol. Lett.*, (CC-BY version 4.0); bottom ©Brandon Cole/naturepl.com; p.43 ©Wild Wonders of Europe/Lundgren/naturepl.com; p.44 © Kaschner et al. (2011) *PLoS ONE*; bottom © Kaschner et al. (2012) *PLos ONE*; p.48 ©Cornell Lab Bioacoustics Research Program; p.49 © Hammond et al. (2013) *Biological Conservation*; pp.50 and 68 ©NOAA; p.55 top left Moira Brown/New England Aquarium, via Wikimedia Commons; bottom right ©Hanne&Jens Eriksen/naturepl.com; pp.57 and 90 bottom ©Todd Pusser; p.58©Augusto Leandro Stanzani/ardea.com; p.63 ©NOAA Sanctuaries Collection; p.64 left ©Reisinger et al. (2014) *PLoS ONE*; right ©Mate et al. (2007) *Deep Sea Research II*; pp.66 and 73 ©Sascha Hooker; p.69 ©Hooker et al. (2012) *Proc. R. Soc. B*; p.70 ©Dr. Mridula Srinivasan, NOAA/NMFS/OST/AMD; p.74 ©DAERA Marine and Fisheries Division; p.77 ©Gabriel Rojo/naturepl.com; p. 77 top ©NERC/BAS; bottom ©Doc White/naturepl.com; pp.80 and 124 ©Flip Nicklin/Minden Pictures; p.81 top ©Laurent Geslin/naturepl.com; p.85 ©Madsen et al. (2013) *J. Comp. Physiol. A*; p.86 bottom ©Vicki Beaver/Ocean Alliance; pp.90 top and 95 top ©Tony Wu/naturepl.com; p.91 ©Rebecca Wellard;p.92 Adapted from By Phoenix_PNX (Own work) [CC BY-SA 3.0 (http://creativecommons.org/licenses/by-sa/3.0)], via Wikimedia Commons; p.93 bottom ©Estes et al (2011) *Science*; p. 95 bottom © NOAA/NOS/NMS/CINMS/National Marine Sanctuaries Media Library; p.96 ©Paul Souders/Danita Delimonth/ardea.com; p.97 left ©Craig Smith, University of Hawaii; p.98 ©Brandon Cole/naturepl.com; p.100 ©Jennifer Allen; p.101 ©Allen et al. (2013) *Science*; p.103 ©Augusto Leandro Stanzani/ardea.com; p.104 © Richards, Wolz and Herman (1984) *J. Comp. Psychol.*; p.105 bottom ©Garland et al. (2011) *Current Biology*; p.108 ©Filatova et al. (2013) *Behavioural Processes*; p.109 ©Luis Quinta/naturepl.com; p.110 Kristian Berge [No restrictions], via Wikimedia Commons; p.112 ©New Bedford Whaling Museum; p113 top ©Wellcome Library, London; middle David Stanley from Nanaimo, Canada [CC BY 2.0 (http://creativecommons.org/licenses/by/2.0), via Wikimedia Commons; bottom Australian Customs and Border Protection Service [CC BY-SA 3.0 au (http://creativecommons.org/licenses/by-sa/3.0/au/deed.en)], via Wikimedia Commons; p.117 Cybjorg at English Wikipedia GFDL (http://www.gnu.org/copyleft/fdl.html) or CC-BY-SA-3.0 (http://creativecommons.org/licenses/by-sa/3.0/)], via Wikimedia Commons; p.119 Jurgen Freund/naturepl.com; p.120 S. Newrick (Own work) [CC BY SA 4.0 (http://creativecommons.org/licenses/by-sa/4.0)], via Wikimedia Commons; p.121 AngeloGandolfi/naturepl.com;p.122 ©Steven Kazlowski/naturepl.com; p.125 ©Florida Fish and Wildlife Conservation Commission; p.126 ©fdastudillo/istock; p.127 © Dr. Alexandros Frantzis; p.128 ©Franco Banfi/naturepl.com; p.129 ©roclwyr/istock; p.131 ©Splash247; p.132 ©Cornell Lab Bioacoustics Research Program; p.134 ©Eric Baccega/naturepl.com; p.135 ©Kaschner et al. (2011) *PLoS ONE*.

Unless otherwise stated images are copyright of The Trustees of the Natural History Museum, London. Every effort has been made to contact and accurately credit all copyright holders. If we have been unsuccessful, we apologise and welcome correction for future editions and reprints.

AUTHORS' ACKNOWLEDGEMENTS

We are indebted to our colleagues at the Sea Mammal Research Unit, University of St Andrews, whose stimulating discussions over the years have increased our knowledge and understanding, and helped to shape our perspectives on cetacean biology and conservation. We are grateful to our colleagues around the world who responded to our requests for personal research images, whether included in the book or not. PT gratefully acknowledges funding from the Marine Alliance for Science and Technology for Scotland, which is funded by the Scottish Funding Council (grant reference HR09011) and contributing institutions. Finally, we thank Trudy Brannan and the editorial team at the Natural History Museum for approaching us to write this book and for guiding us through the process to publication.